# Sustainable Geotechnics

# Sustainable Geotechnics—Theory, Practice, and Applications

Editor

**Slobodan B. Mickovski**

MDPI • Basel • Beijing • Wuhan • Barcelona • Belgrade • Manchester • Tokyo • Cluj • Tianjin

*Editor*
Slobodan B. Mickovski
Glasgow Caledonian University
UK

*Editorial Office*
MDPI
St. Alban-Anlage 66
4052 Basel, Switzerland

This is a reprint of articles from the Special Issue published online in the open access journal *Sustainability* (ISSN 2071-1050) (available at: https://www.mdpi.com/journal/sustainability/special_issues/sustainable_geotechnics).

For citation purposes, cite each article independently as indicated on the article page online and as indicated below:

| LastName, A.A.; LastName, B.B.; LastName, C.C. Article Title. *Journal Name* **Year**, *Volume Number*, Page Range. |
|---|

**ISBN 978-3-0365-1479-6 (Hbk)**
**ISBN 978-3-0365-1480-2 (PDF)**

Cover image courtesy of Slobodan B. Mickovski

# Contents

# About the Editor

**Slobodan B. Mickovski** PhD, MSc, BSc(Hons) is a Professor of Civil Engineering and Environmental Technology at the Glasgow Caledonian University. He is an experienced academic with substantial civil and geotechnical engineering background who has worked in sectors including rail, highways, flood defence, marine, residential developments and car parks, erosion protection and forestry. He has specialist expertise in ground bio- and eco-engineering solutions and erosion protection through sustainable use of vegetation including vegetated natural or man-made slopes, nature-based solutions, and natural hazard remediation. He works with a range of clients and provides advice to senior executives and managers at a strategic level.

*Editorial*

# Sustainable Geotechnics—Theory, Practice, and Applications

**Slobodan B. Mickovski**

Department of Civil Engineering and Environmental Management, School of Computing, Engineering and Built Environment, Glasgow Caledonian University, Glasgow G4 0BA, UK; slobodan.mickovski@gcu.ac.uk

Today, modern Geotechnical Engineers, who in the past would have considered the phenomena occurring in the (primarily soil) environment, are faced with developments in environmental sciences that are becoming more and more detailed and sophisticated, with the natural phenomena and processes surrounding the civil engineering infrastructure being modelled, designed, monitored, and assessed in a more holistic way. This Special Issue aimed to bring together the state of the art in Geotechnics with a focus on sustainable design, construction, and monitoring of the performance of geotechnical assets from ground investigations through foundation and drainage design, to soil stabilization and reinforcement. Submissions from engineers and scientists working in the fields of green infrastructure, nature-based solutions, sustainable drainage, eco-engineering, hydro-geology, landscape planning, plant science, environmental biology or bio-chemistry, earth sciences, GIS, and remote sensing were solicited to highlight significant geotechnical components or applications. Case studies showcasing the application of the sustainable development principles (e.g., reuse, recycle, reduce; stakeholder engagement; public health; UN Global Sustainability Goals) in Geotechnics were also welcomed.

This Special Issue was a success in terms of engaging with geotechnical engineers and researchers worldwide who have keen interest in a wide variety of geotechnical issues and are willing to share their experience and expertise in application of the sustainable development concepts in their work. As a result, in this Special Issue, you will be able to read about potential sustainable approaches in transportation geotechnics, urban environment and water resource management.

Attempting to summarize and highlight the points made in this Special Issue, without spoiling the pleasure of reading the papers for you, I would start with a basic concept in Geotechnical Engineering—the shear strength of soils—which is the *fil rouge* which accompanies the reader through this volume.

Pham and co-authors [1] present a novel hybrid soft computing model using Random Forest and Particle Swarm Optimization for estimation of undrained shear strength of soil based on the clay content, moisture content, specific gravity, void ratio, liquid limit, and plastic limit. Applicable to the whole design range of geotechnical engineering (e.g., foundation design, earth and rock fill dam design, highway and airfield design, stability of slopes and cuts, and in the design of coastal structures), this model is based on the experimental results of 127 soil samples from a national highway project in Vietnam, and they were used to generate datasets for training and validating the model. The results of the model comparison showed that the proposed hybrid model has a high accuracy in the prediction of shear strength of soil and is superior to the single RF model without optimization. Thus, the proposed hybrid model (RF-PSO) can be used for accurate estimation of shear strength, which can be used for the suitable designing of civil engineering structures.

Without adequate shear strength of the soil, the effects of climate change, combined with the urbanization and other anthropogenic effects, will adversely affect the stability of natural and man-made infrastructure, as demonstrated in the study by Bezzera et al. [2], who used sustainable techniques for mapping landslides in an urban area in Brazil. Landslides are part of the natural processes occurring on the Earth's surface, and their occurrence is accelerated and triggered by anthropic interference. Inadequate occupation of areas

**Citation:** Mickovski, S.B. Sustainable Geotechnics—Theory, Practice, and Applications. *Sustainability* **2021**, *13*, 5286. https://doi.org/10.3390/su13095286

Received: 4 May 2021
Accepted: 7 May 2021
Published: 9 May 2021

**Publisher's Note:** MDPI stays neutral with regard to jurisdictional claims in published maps and institutional affiliations.

highly susceptible to landslide processes is shown to be the principal cause of accidents on Brazilian urban slopes, especially those occupied by settlements and slums. In their study, Bezzera and co-workers showed that the existence of areas with steep and densely occupied slopes makes the entirety of the municipality area susceptible to landslides. In this context, their study aimed to map the risk of landslides in an urban area using a quali-quantitative model which applies a multicriteria analytical hierarchy process (AHP) to a Geographic Information System (GIS), 11 risk indicators were submitted to pairwise comparisons by 10 risk management specialists in order to determine the relative importance (weighting) for each of these factors as a function of their contribution to the risk. The weightings obtained were combined to produce the final risk map of the study area, using a map algebra framework. The results showed that there is an existing critical risk for the resident population, and to the sustainability in general, primarily related to the possibility of a landslide, with potentially negative economic, environmental, and mainly social impacts.

To improve the strength of the soil and minimize the risks of such natural disasters, novel, sustainable materials are needed. Liu and co-workers [3] used calcium sulfoaluminate cement (CSA) to stabilize a type of marine soft soil in China. They tested the unconfined compressive strength (UCS) of CSA-stabilized soil and compared it to ordinary Portland cement (OPC); meanwhile the influence of amounts of gypsum in CSA and cement contents in stabilized soils on the strength of stabilized soils were investigated. X-ray diffraction (XRD) tests were employed to detect generated hydration products, and scanning electron microscopy (SEM) was conducted to analyze microstructures of CSA-stabilized soils. The results of their study, while offering an insight into the micro-structure of stabilized soils, also showed that UCS of CSA-stabilized soils firstly increased and then decreased with contents of gypsum increasing from 0 to 40 wt.%, and CSA-stabilized soils exhibited the highest UCS when the content of gypsum equaled 25 wt.%. Similarly, Cislaghi et al. [4] present a case for biodegradable geogrids leading towards more sustainable materials for geo-environmental engineering. While plastic materials are widely used in geotechnical engineering, especially as geosynthetics, the use of plastic-based products involves serious environmental risks caused by their degradation. The research presented here was focused on biodegradable polymers of natural origin, especially on polylactic acid (PLA), to reduce the use of plastics. Their study aimed to explore the potentiality of biopolymers for the production of geogrids, measuring the chemical and mechanical characteristics of raw materials and of prototype samples, similar to those available on the market. First, chemical composition and optical purity were determined by hydrogen nuclear magnetic resonance (1H-NMR) and polarimetry. Furthermore, samples of uniaxial and biaxial geogrids were custom-molded using a professional 3D printer. Mechanical properties were measured both on the filament and on the prototype geogrids. The results of this study showed that the maximum tensile resistance for the neat-PLA filament was smaller than the one for uniaxial prototype geogrids produced with PLA-based polymers mixed with titanium dioxide. PLA-based materials showed higher tensile properties than polypropylene (PP), the most common petroleum derivative. Conversely, such biomaterials seem to be more brittle and have a scarce elongation rate with respect to PP. Nonetheless, the results of this study are encouraging and can support the use of PLA-based materials for innovative biodegradable geosynthetics production, especially if used sustainably in combination with live plants.

However, sustainable materials contributing to the increase in soil strength would have little value without appropriate planning and design procedures and strategies. On those lines, Al-Janabi et al. [5] offer a case study for experimental and numerical analysis for earth-fill dam seepage, while Wallace et al. [6] demonstrate how adopting erosion control measures can reduce the land required to accommodate temporary and permanent sustainable drainage measures.

In the former study, earth-fill dams, which are the most common and most economical type of dam, but also more vulnerable to internal erosion and piping due to seepage problems, which are the main causes of dam failure, are analyzed in terms of seepage using physical, mathematical, and numerical models. The results from the three methods revealed that both mathematical calculations and the numerical model have a conjectured seepage line compatible with the observed seepage line in the physical model. However, when the seepage flow intersected the downstream slope and when piping took place, the use of numerical modelling to calculate the flow rate became obsolete as it was unable to calculate the volume of water flow in pipes. This was revealed by the big difference in results between physical and numerical models in the first physical model, while the results were compatible in the second physical model when the seepage line stayed within the body of the dam and low compacted soil was adopted. Numerical seepage analysis for seven different configurations of an earth-fill dam (four homogenous dams and three zoned dams) was conducted at normal and maximum water levels to find the most appropriate configuration among them. This revealed that if a sufficient quantity of silty sand soil is available around the proposed dam location, a homogenous earth-fill dam with a medium drain length of 0.5 m thickness is the best design configuration. Otherwise, a zoned earth-fill dam with a central core and 1:0.5 Horizontal to Vertical ratio (H:V) would be preferable.

In the latter study, Wallace et al. [6] demonstrate the development of a methodological Framework for estimating temporary drainage capacity to inform land requirements for a highway construction project in Scotland. Silt pollution generated during major highway construction projects can prove detrimental to the water environment and the aquatic species that depend on it. Construction activities can leave many kilometers of exposed soil susceptible to erosion from surface water runoff, which can result in silt pollution and degradation of ecologically sensitive watercourses if appropriate mitigation is not in place. In Scotland, assurances need to be provided during scheme development to demonstrate that there is sufficient space to accommodate temporary drainage. In response, a methodological framework has been developed that can be applied before construction commences to estimate the required capacity of settlement ponds, including runoff and soil loss volume estimation. The application of the framework as a case-study demonstrated the potential applicability of the approach and highlighted where further refinements can be made to increase the robustness for future applications by improving the accuracy of input parameters to address site-specific conditions. Furthermore, it demonstrated how adopting erosion control measures can reduce the land required to accommodate sustainable drainage measures, such as temporary settlement ponds.

Bearing in mind that the geographical spread of the research presented in this Special Issue includes Asia, South America, and Europe, it is clear that there is solid awareness of the sustainability in Geotechnical Engineering worldwide, and the geotechnical engineers and researchers work tirelessly to provide innovative solutions for the infrastructure, which should resist the effects of climate change and can be applied worldwide. However, to successfully combat the growing climate change challenges and work towards sustainable and healthy communities, geotechnical engineers should embrace the sustainability approaches (e.g., green infrastructure, nature-based solutions, ground bio-engineering, sustainable drainage; Mickovski [7]) while aiming for the achievement of multiple sustainable development goals. Ending this Editorial, I would encourage you to browse through this Special Issue and thank you for continuing support of sustainability in Geotechnics.

**Conflicts of Interest:** The author declares no conflict of interest.

## References

1. Pham, B.T.; Qi, C.; Ho, L.S.; Nguyen-Thoi, T.; Al-Ansari, N.; Nguyen, M.D.; Nguyen, H.D.; Ly, H.B.; Le, H.V.; Prakash, I. A Novel Hybrid Soft Computing Model Using Random Forest and Particle Swarm Optimization for Estimation of Undrained Shear Strength of Soil. *Sustainability* **2020**, *12*, 2218. [CrossRef]
2. Bezerra, L.; Neto, O.F.; Santos, O., Jr.; Mickovski, S.B. Landslide Risk Mapping in an Urban Area of the City of Natal, Brazil. *Sustainability* **2020**, *12*, 9601. [CrossRef]
3. Liu, H.; Zhao, J.; Wang, Y.; Yi, N.; Cui, C. Strength Performance and Microstructure of Calcium Sulfoaluminate Cement-Stabilized Soft Soil. *Sustainability* **2021**, *13*, 2295. [CrossRef]

4. Cislaghi, A.; Sala, P.; Borgonovo, G.; Gandolfi, C.; Bischetti, G.B. Towards More Sustainable Materials for Geo-Environmental Engineering: The Case of Geogrids. *Sustainability* **2021**, *13*, 2585. [CrossRef]
5. Al-Janabi, A.M.S.; Ghazali, A.H.; Ghazaw, Y.M.; Afan, H.A.; Al-Ansari, N.; Yaseen, Z.M. Experimental and Numerical Analysis for Earth-Fill Dam Seepage. *Sustainability* **2020**, *12*, 2490. [CrossRef]
6. Wallace, M.; Meldrum, A.; Mickovski, S.B.; McNee, I.; Lear, D.; Flint, S. Developing a Methodological Framework for Estimating Temporary Drainage Capacity to Inform Land Requirements for a Highway Construction Project in Scotland. *Sustainability* **2020**, *12*, 5522. [CrossRef]
7. Mickovski, S.B. Re-Thinking Soil Bioengineering to Address Climate Change Challenges. *Sustainability* **2021**, *13*, 3338. [CrossRef]

*Article*

# A Novel Hybrid Soft Computing Model Using Random Forest and Particle Swarm Optimization for Estimation of Undrained Shear Strength of Soil

**Binh Thai Pham [1,2], Chongchong Qi [3], Lanh Si Ho [4], Trung Nguyen-Thoi [1,2], Nadhir Al-Ansari [5,*], Manh Duc Nguyen [6], Huu Duy Nguyen [7], Hai-Bang Ly [8,*], Hiep Van Le [9,*] and Indra Prakash [10]**

1. Division of Computational Mathematics and Engineering, Institute for Computational Science, Ton Duc Thang University, Ho Chi Minh 700000, Vietnam; phamthaibinh@tdtu.edu.vn (B.T.P.); nguyenthoitrung@tdtu.edu.vn (T.N.-T.)
2. Faculty of Civil Engineering, Ton Duc Thang University, Ho Chi Minh 700000, Vietnam
3. School of Resources and Safety Engineering, Central South University, Changsha 410083, China; chongchong.qi@gmail.com
4. Department of Civil and Environmental Engineering, Graduate School of Engineering, Hiroshima University, Hiroshima 739-527, Japan; hosilanh@hiroshima-u.ac.jp
5. Department of Civil, Environmental and Natural Resources Engineering, Lulea University of Technology, 971 87 Lulea, Sweden
6. University of Transport and Communications, Hanoi 100000, Vietnam; nguyenducmanh@utc.edu.vn
7. Faculty of Geography, VNU University of Science, Vietnam National University, Hanoi 100000, Vietnam; huuduy151189@gmail.com
8. University of Transport and Technology, Hanoi 100000, Vietnam
9. Institute of Research and Development, Duy Tan University, Da Nang 550000, Vietnam
10. Department of Science & Technology, Bhaskarcharya Institute for Space Applications and Geo-Informatics (BISAG), Government of Gujarat, Gandhinagar 382007, India; indra52prakash@gmail.com

* Correspondence: nadhir.alansari@ltu.se (N.A.-A.); banglh@utt.edu.vn (H.-B.L.); levanhiep2@duytan.edu.vn (H.V.L.)

Received: 8 February 2020; Accepted: 11 March 2020; Published: 12 March 2020

**Abstract:** Determination of shear strength of soil is very important in civil engineering for foundation design, earth and rock fill dam design, highway and airfield design, stability of slopes and cuts, and in the design of coastal structures. In this study, a novel hybrid soft computing model (RF-PSO) of random forest (RF) and particle swarm optimization (PSO) was developed and used to estimate the undrained shear strength of soil based on the clay content (%), moisture content (%), specific gravity (%), void ratio (%), liquid limit (%), and plastic limit (%). In this study, the experimental results of 127 soil samples from national highway project Hai Phong-Thai Binh of Vietnam were used to generate datasets for training and validating models. Pearson correlation coefficient (R) method was used to evaluate and compare performance of the proposed model with single RF model. The results show that the proposed hybrid model (RF-PSO) achieved a high accuracy performance (R = 0.89) in the prediction of shear strength of soil. Validation of the models also indicated that RF-PSO model (R = 0.89 and Root Mean Square Error (RMSE) = 0.453) is superior to the single RF model without optimization (R = 0.87 and RMSE = 0.48). Thus, the proposed hybrid model (RF-PSO) can be used for accurate estimation of shear strength which can be used for the suitable designing of civil engineering structures.

**Keywords:** machine learning; random forest; particle swarm optimization; Vietnam

## 1. Introduction

In civil engineering, the shear strength of the soil is an essential engineering property in the foundation design and stability analysis of all major construction projects such as dams, bridges, highways and road, railway lines, jetties, underground structures, and high-rise buildings [1,2]. It is well-known that the shear strength of soil is governed by interlocking between soil particles, frictional resistance, and cohesion of soil particles. Soil is a complicated material containing soil particles of different sizes and minerals, water, air, and void. The shear strength of soil is influenced by soil constituents, specific gravity, void ratio, moisture content (liquid and plastic limits), clay content, stress history, and relative density. The shear strength parameters are usually determined in the laboratory using direct shear test, unconfined compression test, and triaxial compression test and also in the field by shear vane test, Standard Penetration Test (SPT) and in situ-shear test [3,4]. In addition to these tests, the estimation of the shear strength of soil from other indirect methods is needed for quick and reliable results. Many researchers have attempted to estimate the shear strength of soil using different alternative methods [3,5–10]. The shear strength of unsaturated soil can also be predicted using the empirical correlation function [10,11], using soil-water retention curve [10,12,13].

Nowadays, soft computing techniques of machine learning (ML) or artificial intelligence (AI) have been widely used in many scientific, medical, and engineering fields including geotechnical engineering [14–26]. Sharma et al. [27] used Artificial Neuron Network (ANN) in estimating elasticity modulus of soil. Kalkan et al. [28] used Adaptive Neuro Fuzzy Inference System (ANFIS) and ANN methods for the prediction of compressive strength of compacted granular soils. They concluded that the ANFIS model gave a promising solution for predicting the compressive strength of the compacted soil. Other researchers have used several algorithms of ML namely Support Vector Regression (SVR) and its hybridization with Particle Swarm Optimization (PSO-SVR) [29] using some basic parameters such as water content, clay content, consistency limits, etc. [30]. Pham et al. [31] also developed and used Parsimonious Network based on a Fuzzy Inference System (PANFIS) hybrid ML model in the prediction of soil shear strength.

Random forest (RF) first introduced by Breiman for solving regression, unsupervised learning, and classification problems [32,33], is a powerful ML technique which has been applied successfully in many classification problems including geotechnical engineering [29]. However, for excellent RF modeling, fine-tuning of its hyperparameters is required by optimization algorithms. There are some good optimization algorithms that are usually employed in solving geotechnical engineering problems such as Particle Swarm Optimization (PSO), Genetic Algorithm (GA), Ant Colony Optimization (ACO), Firefly Algorithm (FA), and Artificial Bee Colony (ABC). Out of these algorithms, the PSO is one of the most popular optimization techniques that has been mostly used in geotechnical engineering including slope stability and foundation engineering [27,34–37].

The main objective of the present study is to develop a novel hybrid soft computing model RF-PSO using goodness of individual models, namely RF and PSO, for the quick and better estimation of undrained shear strength of soil, based on the basic soil parameters such as moisture content, clay content, consistency limits, and Atterberg limit. The novelty of this study is that a hybrid model PSO-RF was developed the first time for better estimation of the shear strength of soil from basic parameters. For this, one of the national highway projects, Hai Phong-Thai Binh of Vietnam, was selected as a study area considering its importance and availability of the sufficient soil mechanics data for the development and validation of the model. Pearson correlation coefficient (R) and Root Mean Square Error (RMSE) methods were used to validate the model and sensitivity analysis was carried out to analyze the relationship between shear strength and influencing factors.

## 2. Case Study and Data Collection

### 2.1. Description of the Study Area

The study area is located along alignment of Hai Phong-Thai Binh coastal national highway, Vietnam. The total length of the highway project is approximately 29.7 km, which covers 20.782 km towards Hai Phong city side and 8.928 km towards Thai Binh province side (Figure 1). In this route, construction of eight bridges will be implemented. Two bridges on this alignment are large bridges with the length of 2 km and 1 km will cross over Van Uc and Thai Binh river, respectively. A total of 127 soil samples in this study were collected from the construction project of Hai Phong-Thai Binh coastal national highway for the estimation of soil shear strength and model study. The soil investigations carried out in this project included the following field tests: Standard Penetration Test (SPT), boring test, shear vane test, and laboratory tests (direct shear test and triaxial compression test) for the determination of engineering properties of soil [3,4]. However, only data of direct shear test with Undrained and Unconfined (UU) scheme [38] was used for this modeling study.

### 2.2. Data Used

#### 2.2.1. Output (Undrained Shear Strength of Soil)

Output of this study is the undrained total normal shear strength parameter of soil. Shear strength of soil is defined as the maximum resistance per unit of soil that can mobilize to resist the shear stress causing the sliding failure in any plane of a soil mass. Shear strength of soil is known as an important parameter which is used in the design and analysis of stability problems of civil engineering structures. The sliding failure is related to both normal and shear stress, thus shear strength is considered as a linear function of normal and shear stress [38]. The undrained total normal shear strength ($\tau_f$) is determined using the following equation.

$$\tau_f = c + \sigma \tan \varphi \quad (1)$$

where, $c$, $\varphi$, $\sigma$ are the cohesion, internal friction angle, and normal stress, respectively.

In this study, direct shear tests with UU scheme was carried out to determine the values of undrained total normal shear strength for the modeling. Initial analysis of data used is presented in Table 1.

**Table 1.** Initial analysis of data used in this study.

| No | Parameters | Min Values | Max Values | Mean Values | Standard Deviation |
|---|---|---|---|---|---|
| 1 | Clay content (%) | 1.00 | 47.5 | 25.72 | 10.172 |
| 2 | Water content (%) | 23.04 | 70.74 | 48.3 | 11.73 |
| 3 | Specific gravity | 2.67 | 2.72 | 2.69 | 0.01 |
| 4 | Void ratio | 0.63 | 1.92 | 1.36 | 0.31 |
| 5 | Liquid limit (%) | 26.08 | 79.76 | 53.34 | 13.39 |
| 6 | Plastic limit (%) | 15.36 | 40.48 | 28.38 | 5.01 |
| 7 | Undrained total normal shear strength (kG/cm$^2$) | 0.29 | 0.57 | 0.41 | 0.06 |

#### 2.2.2. Input Variables

Input data used in the model study include physical properties of soil: clay content, specific gravity, void ratio, and Atterberg limit (liquid limit and plastic limit). According to Das and Sobhan [38], the size of the clay particles are less than 0.002 mm. Some researchers have considered clay size range to be less than 0.002 to 0.005 mm [31,38]. The amount of clay particles directly affects the Atterberg limits such as liquid and plastic limits. The soil that contains more clay content could result in high plasticity when it absorbs water, thus leading to a decrease in shear strength parameters such as cohesion c and internal friction angle $\varphi$. The amount of clay can be determined from the grain size test [39].

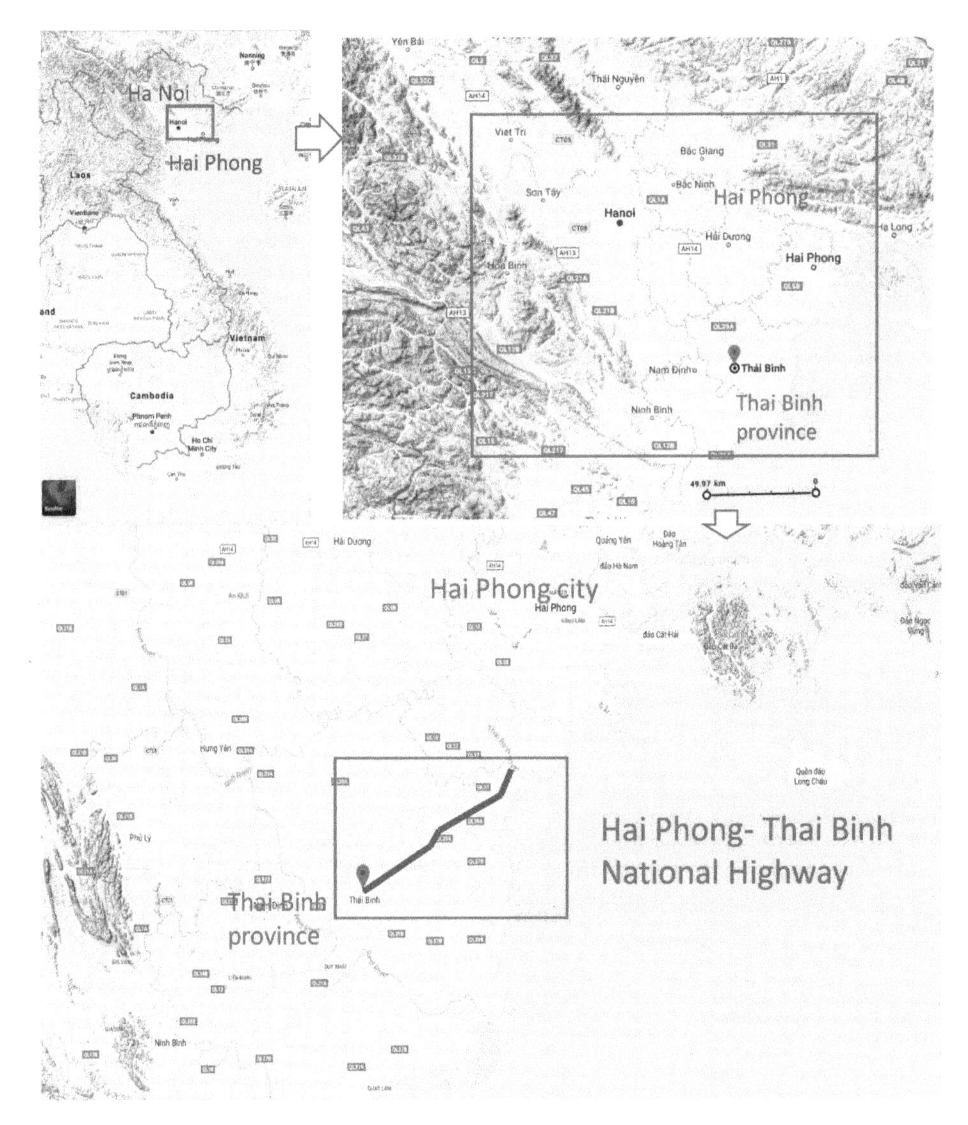


**Figure 1.** Location map of the study area.

Water content has an important role in influencing many soil properties such as strength, elasticity, and hydraulic conductivity [38]. Water content of the soil is governed by environment condition such as temperature, groundwater level, and humidity. With the increase of water content, cohesion between soil particles reduces; thus, the shear strength also decreases. It is well-known that the shear strength of soil is strongly affected by the moisture change, especially soil containing high clay minerals. Thus, in this research, we considered water content as one of the important input parameters for predicting the shear strength of soil. Water content is defined by the ratio between the mass (weight) of water divided to the mass (weight) of dried soil (i.e., soil particle) in a given volume of soil [39].

Specific gravity is a term that is used to compare how much lighter or heavier solid material (soil particles) is compared to water [38]. It is a ratio between the density of solid phase and water density. It is known that specific gravity is related to the density of minerals of soil: if the specific gravity is large, the soil will be denser with higher shear strength. Thus, the specific gravity must be considered as the main factor in predicting shear strength. In the laboratory, the specific gravity is directly determined by measuring density of soil samples using density bottle and Pycnometer methods [39]. Void ratio of soil not only influences the hydraulic conductivity but also affects significantly the shear strength of the soil. When soil has a large void ratio, the shear strength of soil will be small, because the higher void ratio could have a higher moisture content.

Liquid limit is an important parameter which influences the shear strength. The shear strength decreases with the increase of liquid limit [38]. Liquid limit is determined as the moisture content; at that point soil transfers from the plastic to the liquid state. Plastic limit is one of the important factors affecting the soil strength. It is defined as the water content point at which soil transfers states from semisolid to plastic [38]. These Atterberg limits can be determined by Atterberg tests in laboratory [38].

## 3. Methods Used

### 3.1. Random Forest

Random forest (RF) is a powerful method that was first introduced by Breiman for solving regression, unsupervised learning, and classification problems [32,33]. It has been applied in many fields including geotechnical engineering with high performance results [29]. The RF has some advantages such as high accuracy performance with complicated datasets with small calibrating and variables with high noises [40,41]. For the classification problem, Bagging technique is employed in order to arbitrarily choose the variable candidates from the entire dataset for calibrating models [15]. In this research, an Out-Of-Bag (OOB) sample and two kinds of errors (namely decrease in precision and reduction in Gini) were calculated because these errors can be adopted to rank and select variables [42,43]. Regarding each variable, when the variable values are transposed across the OOB observations, the function decides the error of prediction model [44].

### 3.2. Particle Swarm Optimization (PSO)

The PSO is a computational method which is a form of evolution algorithm such as GA and ant colony algorithm used in the optimization problem, initially proposed by Eberhart and Kennedy [45]. This algorithm differs from the GA as it focuses more on the interaction between individuals in a population to explore search space. The PSO is a result of modeling bird flying to find food; thus, it uses swarm intelligence. This algorithm is a powerful technique that has been employed commonly for optimization problems in many fields, especially in geotechnical engineering [14,31,46]. The PSO works with a random population of particles, in which each particle is considered as a given approach to seek a solution for solving the problem. The PSO includes a group of particles, each particle in a group moves indiscriminately in a research space and is affected by surrounding position during movement [47,48]. The result of each particle position is affected by its knowledge and the knowledge of its neighbors. Thus, it can be said that in a swarm the knowledge of other particles can influence the searching method of a particle. For each iteration, the position of each particle is upgraded considering its current position and velocity [35,49]. The next swarm was established in accordance with the updated particle positions considering their own best position ($P_{best}$) in search space and the whole swarm best position ($G_{best}$). The particle position and velocities are computed as follows:

$$V_i^{t+1} = wV_i^t + m_1 n_1 (p_{best,i}^t - Y_i^t) + m_2 n_2 (g_{best,i}^t - Y_i^t) \tag{2}$$

$$Y_i^{t+1} = Y_i^t + V_i^{t+1} \tag{3}$$

where $V_i^t$ and $V_i^{t+1}$ denote velocities of particle $i$ at iteration $t$ and $t+1$, respectively; whereas, $Y_i^t$ and $Y_i^{t+1}$ represent positions of particle $i$ at repetition $t$ and $t+1$; $w$, $m_1$, *and* $m_2$ correspond to the cognitive, social effect, and inertia parameters, respectively; $n_1$ and $n_2$ indicate arbitrary numbers with the range of [0, 1]; $p_{best,i}^t$ and $g_{best,i}^t$ symbolize the best position of particle $i$ and swarm, respectively.

The best position of particle and swarm in the following iteration is defined as follows:

$$p_{best,i}^{t+1} = \begin{cases} Y_i^{t+1}, h\left(Y_i^{t+1}\right) < h\left(p_{best,i}^t\right) \\ p_{best,i}^t, h\left(Y_i^{t+1}\right) \geq h\left(p_{best,i}^t\right) \end{cases} \quad (4)$$

$$g_{best}^{t+1} = \operatorname{argmin}\left\{h\left(p_{best,0}^{t+1}\right), \ldots, h\left(p_{best,ns}^{t+1}\right), h\left(g_{best}^t\right)\right\} \quad (5)$$

where *ns* indicate the summation of particles in a swarm.

### 3.3. Dataset Splitting

In the modeling, clay content, moisture content, specific gravity, void ratio, liquid limit, and plastic limit were used as input, whereas the undrained total normal shear strength of soil was used as an output. In other words, there were six inputs and one output for each instance in the dataset. All variables were normalized into (0, 1) range based on their maximum and minimum values.

For supervised learning, the dataset of 127 soil samples needs to be split into two parts. The first part is used for model training and hyperparameter tuning, which is known as the training set. The second part is known as the testing set used for model verification. As the size of the training set will have an important influence on the performance of ML modeling [49], to ascertain the best training set size (TSS) for the preparation of shear strength dataset, the TSS was changed from 30% to 90%. The RF performance was calculated with the default hyperparameters from Scikit-learn [50]. For each TSS, 100 RF models were built and the average performance was calculated to reduce the randomness in random splitting.

It is important to note that the performance on the training set was calculated using 5-fold CV validation. In terms of the performance on the testing set, the whole training set was first used to train the RF model, with which the prediction on the testing set was obtained. In other words, the prediction on the training set was obtained using the RF model trained with part of the training set, compared with the whole training set during the prediction on the testing set. Thus, the prediction on the testing set is usually better than that on the training set if the same prediction method is used [49].

### 3.4. Modeling and Hyperparameters Tuning

In the current study, the RF is utilized to model the nonlinear relationship from the inputs to the output. In order to obtain the expert performance, the hyperparameters of RF were tuned using the PSO. Five important hyperparameters were tuned as suggested in the literature [51]. Table 2 summarizes the tuned hyperparameters, the definition, and their tuning ranges. For each set of hyperparameters, 10 RF models were built to reduce the randomness of random splitting. The number of particles was set to be 100 in the PSO. Moreover, the maximum iteration, inertia parameter, the cognitive influence parameter, and the social influence parameter were set to be 50, 0.7298, 1.49618, and 1.49618, respectively. All parameter setting in the PSO was determined by trial tests [52–55].

**Table 2.** Hyperparameters description and their tuning range.

| No | Hyperparameters | Explanation | Range |
|---|---|---|---|
| 1 | Max_depth | The maximum depth of DTs. | 1–20 |
| 2 | Min_samples_split | The minimum number of samples for the split. | 2–10 |
| 3 | Min_samples_leaf | The minimum number of samples at the leaf node. | 1–10 |
| 4 | Max_DT | The maximum number of RT models in the ensemble | 1–1000 |
| 5 | Max_features | The number of features considered during the selection of the best splitting | 0.4–1 |

During the hyperparameters tuning, the training performance from 5-fold CV was used as the fitness function of the PSO. Each set of hyperparameters was represented by a particle in the PSO. With the iteration of PSO, particle positions would be updated to maximize the fitness value and the hyperparameters were optimized accordingly. The optimum hyperparameters were selected after the PSO. Finally, the RF model with the optimum hyperparameters was verified on the testing set.

### *3.5. RF Model Assessment*

The RF model assessment of this study was carried out using Pearson correlation coefficient (R) and Root Mean Square Error (RMSE) criteria, which are the most common indicators for validation and comparison of machine learning models [22,56–58]. Basically, R presents the correlation between the actual and predicted outputs. Values of R range from −1 to 1, and higher absolute values of R close to 1 indicate better prediction accuracy and vice versa. While RMSE measures the average squared difference between actual and predicted outputs [59–62]. Lower value of RMSE indicates better performance of the model. These indicators are expressed in equations as follows [63–67]:

$$R = \frac{\sum_{i=1}^{m}\left(SS_{coi} - \overline{SS_{co}}\right)\left(SS_{aci} - \overline{SS_{ac}}\right)}{\sqrt{\sum_{i=1}^{m}\left(SS_{coi} - \overline{SS_{co}}\right)^2\left(SS_{aci} - \overline{SS_{ac}}\right)^2}} \quad (6)$$

$$\text{RMSE} = \sqrt{\frac{1}{m}\sum_{i=1}^{m}\left(SS_{coi} - SS_{aci}\right)^2} \quad (7)$$

where $SS_{coi}$ and $\overline{SS_{co}}$ denote the output value of the sample *i*th and the output average value of the sample calculated according to the model, respectively; $SS_{aci}$ and $\overline{SS_{ac}}$ indicate the actual value of the sample *i*th and the actual average values, respectively; m is the summation of samples.

## 4. Results and Discussion

### *4.1. Influence of Training Set Size (TSS)*

From Figure 2, it can be seen that training performance progressively increased with the increase of TSS. Moreover, the standard deviation from the RF models was decreased with increasing TSS. To be more specific, the average *R* value was increased from 0.71 to 0.84 when the TSS was increased from 30% to 90%. Instead, the *SD* was decreased from 0.11 (TSS = 30%) to 0.03 (TSS = 90%). Above results demonstrate that the training performance was improved and became more stable with the increase of TSS.

In terms of the testing performance, it was increased from 0.79 to 0.87 when the TSS was increased from 30% to 80%. After that, the testing performance was decreased to 0.86 when the TSS was further increased to 90%. Standard Deviation (SD) was evidently increased from 0.08 to 0.12 when the TSS was increased to 80% to 90%. The increase of *SD* indicates that the RF prediction was negatively influenced when the TSS surpassed 80%. Since the testing performance represents the generalization capability of ML models, 80% was selected to be the best TSS in this study.

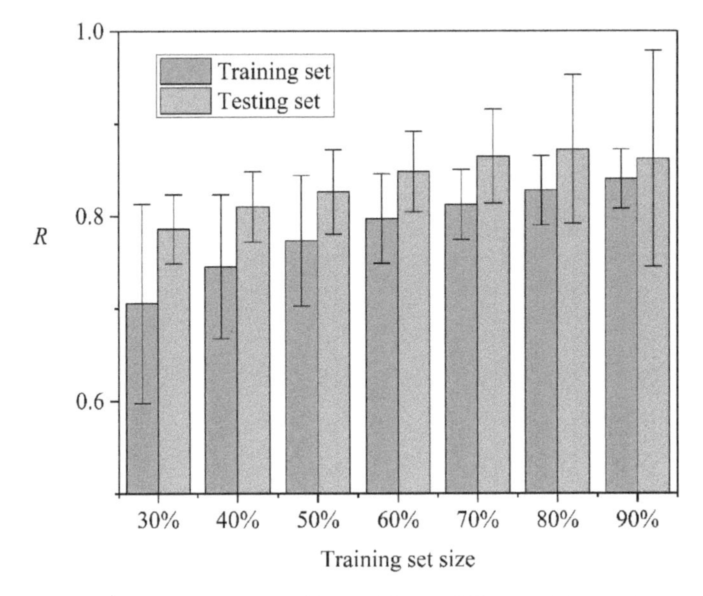


**Figure 2.** Sensitivity analysis of the model using different training set sizes.

### *4.2. Hyperparameters Tuning*

Figure 3 illustrates the highest *R* value ever found by the PSO with iterations. It can be seen that the highest *R* value was progressively increased with the iteration of PSO. The highest *R* was 0.83 at the first iteration, which was increased to 0.88 at the 50th iteration. The optimum RF hyperparameters were determined to be n_estimator = 935, max_depth = 14, min_sample_split = 2, min_samples_leaf = 1, max_features = 0.648.

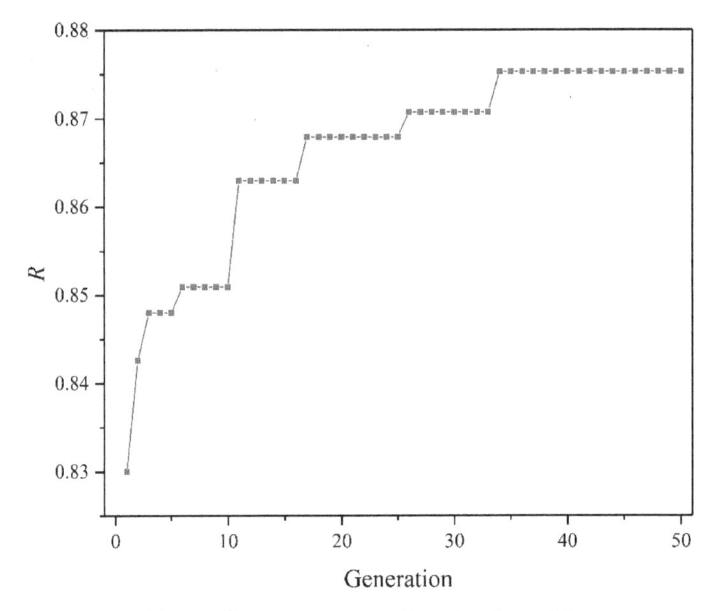


**Figure 3.** Hyperparameters tuning using the model.

*4.3. Predictive Capability of the Models*

Figure 4 presents a visual comparison of the UU based experimental and predicted results from a representative RF model. In this case, the representative RF model was selected since its performance was similar to the average performance from the RF models (Figure 3). The *R* value was 0.87 on the training set and 0.90 on the testing set. It can be seen that there was a good agreement between the experimental and predicted shear strength values, implying the robustness of RF modeling.

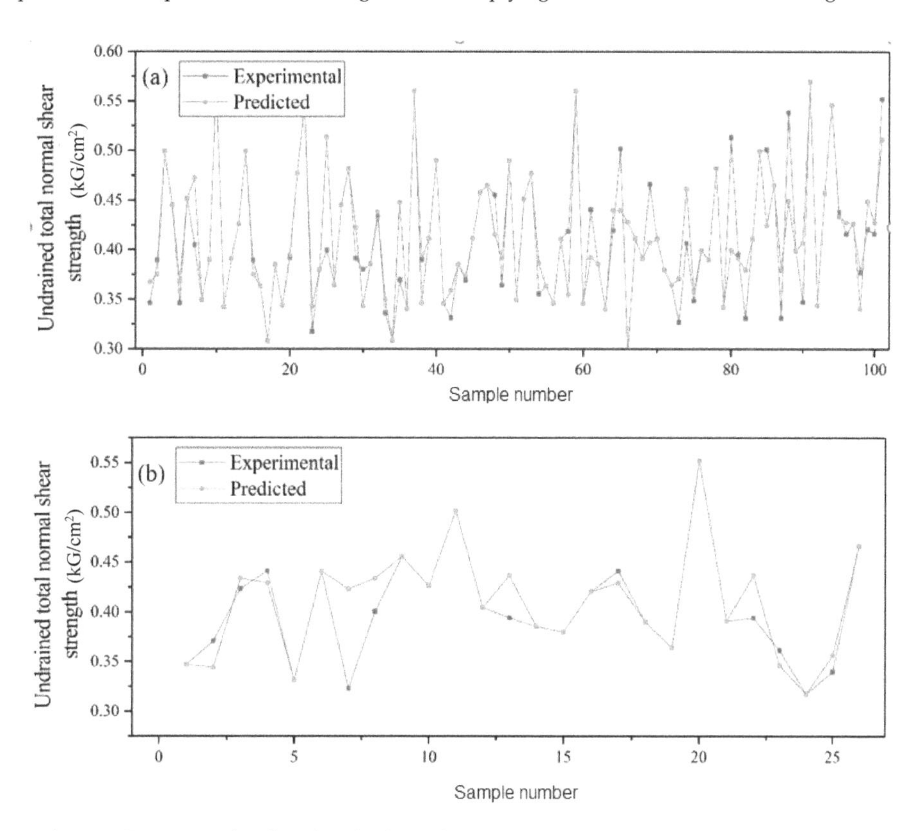


**Figure 4.** Experimental and predicted values of shear strength using the model: (**a**) training set, (**b**) testing set.

Figure 5 demonstrates performance comparison between the RF model with default hyperparameters and the optimum hyperparameters from the PSO (RF-PSO). To obtain more representative results, 100 RF models were constructed and the average performance was compared. It can be seen that the performance of RF modeling was improved after PSO hyperparameters tuning. On the training set, the *R* value was increased from 0.86 to 0.87 after the PSO hyperparameters tuning. At the same time, *SD* was decreased from 0.028 to 0.027, indicating more stable RF modeling. Similar results can be observed on the testing set, where the *R* value was increased (0.87 to 0.89) and *SD* was decreased (0.060 to 0.057). Similarly, the values of RMSE of RF-PSO on both training (0.487) and testing (0.453) is lower than those of sing RF model (0.517 for training and 0.48 for testing) (Table 3). These results confirmed the feasibility of PSO in improving the performance of RF modeling.

**Table 3.** Predictive capability of the models using RMSE criteria.

| No | Models | RMSE | |
|---|---|---|---|
| | | Training | Testing |
| 1 | RF | 0.517 | 0.480 |
| 2 | RF-PSO | 0.487 | 0.453 |

In general, both hybrid model RF-PSO and single RF model performed well for the prediction of undrained shear strength of soil but hybrid model RF-PSO outperforms single RF model. The results are suitable as the RF can measure data structures and classify data, which help focus important variables and remove similar variables. It is not sensitive to unit differences, pointing out that there is no need for a preprocessing process [68]. In addition, the PSO is effectively applied to address the problem of complex optimization as it is automatically to search for optimization solutions and it can easily perform with good efficiency [69]. Thus, it is confirmed that the PSO is an effective optimization technique in improving performance of the RF model.

In general, the proposed RF-PSO model can be used for quick, better prediction of the undrained total normal shear strength of different types of soil. Performance of this model might be different and improved depending on type of soil. One of the advantages of application of hybrid machine learning model (RF-PSO) is that it can handle the big and complicated data. Thus, large or big data can also be analyzed with this model. It is proposed that researchers use large data, depending on the availability, for future model studies.

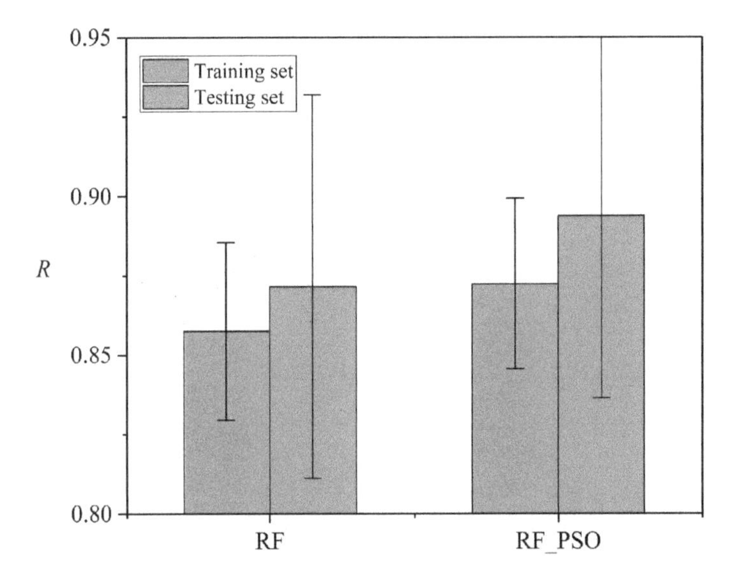


**Figure 5.** Predictive capability of the models.

### 4.4. Sensitivity Analysis of Input Parameters

A sensitivity analysis was carried out to evaluate the importance of input parameters for the modeling using partial dependence plots, which is an efficient way to investigate the relationship between inputs and output. Details are available in the published work [70]. Figure 6 shows the relative importance of the inputs to the output. It can be seen that the moisture content was the most significant variable for the shear strength of soil, which achieved an average importance score of 0.337. The void ratio ranked the second with an average importance score of 0.271, followed by liquid limit (0.166), clay (0.109), and plastic limit (0.093). The specific gravity achieved the smallest average importance score (0.025), indicating that it had the lowest influence on the undrained total normal shear strength of soil.

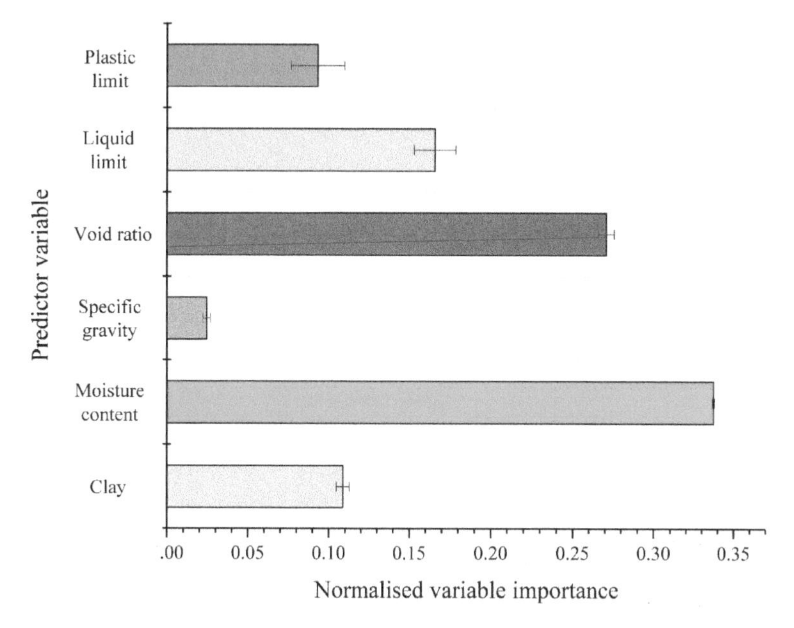


**Figure 6.** Variable importance analysis using the model.

Figure 7 illustrates the partial dependence of the output to the inputs. As shown, the shear strength had an overall negative correlation with clay, moisture content, specific gravity, and void ratio. Moreover, the variation of shear strength was less significant with the variation of specific gravity compared with the variation of clay, moisture content, and void ratio. This result indicates the specific gravity has a relatively lower influence on the undrained shear strength, which agrees well with the important score results (Figure 6). The undrained shear strength decreased first and then increased with the increasing liquid limit. Finally, the undrained shear strength increased with the increase of plastic limit.

In general, out of the input factors, moisture content is considered as the most important factor affecting the undrained shear strength of soil. This is reasonable as the water reduces the friction and cohesion between the soil particles; thus, increase of moisture content leads to decrease of shear strength of soil [31,71].

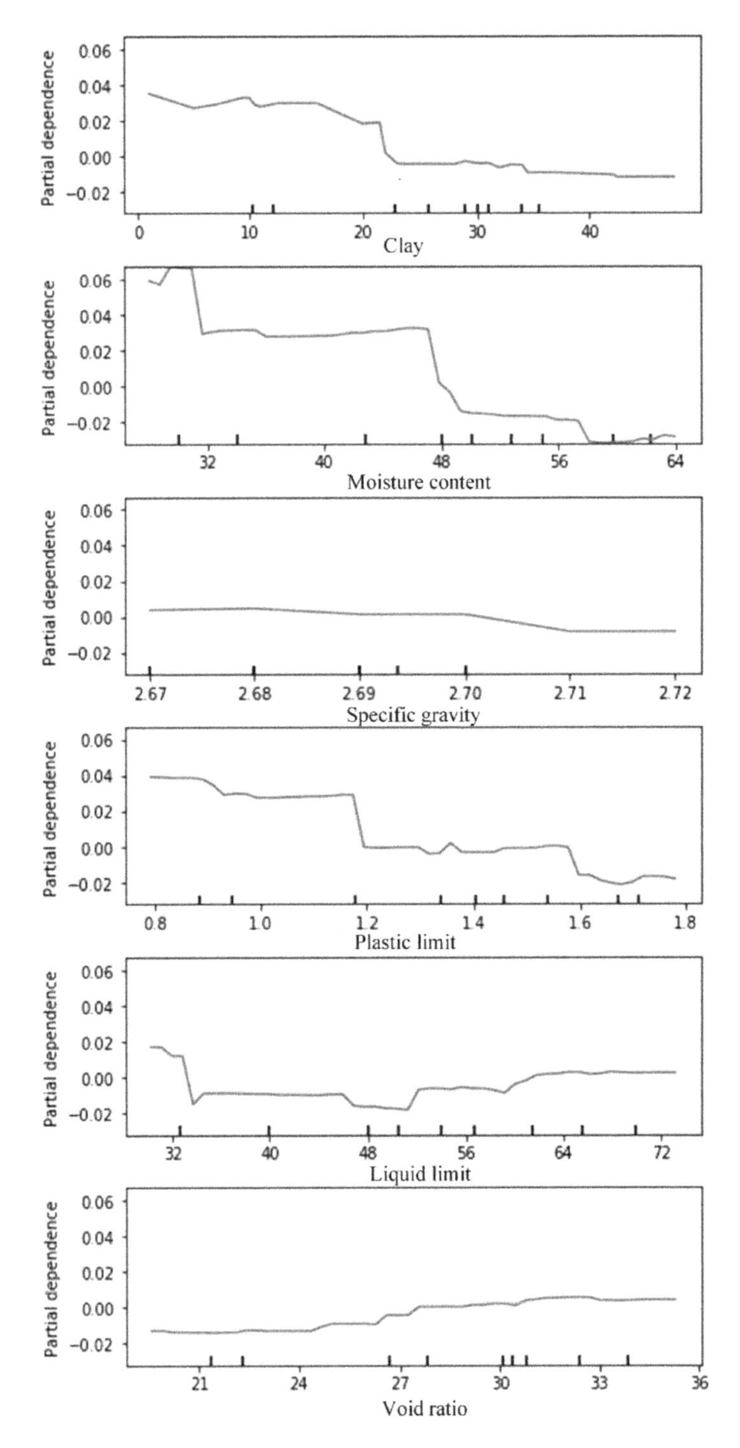


**Figure 7.** Importance of the variables used for the model.

## 5. Conclusions

In this study, a novel hybrid machine learning namely RF-PSO model, which is a combination of RF and PSO models, was proposed and applied to estimate the undrained shear strength of soil for the design purpose of the construction projects. In total, the experimental results of 127 samples were used to create datasets for validating and training models. A statistical measure such as R was used to validate and compare the models. The results show that performance of the models improved and stabilized from 0.79 to 0.84 with the increase of training dataset size from 30% to 80%. Performance of the RF-PSO hybrid model is best with R = 0.89 and RMSE = 0.453, followed by RF with R = 0.87 and RMSE = 0.48 in the estimation of soil shear strength.

In addition, the sensitivity analysis using partial dependence plots was carried out to evaluate the importance of input parameters in the model study. Results show that moisture content is considered as the most important parameter for modeling of prediction of the undrained shear strength though other parameters considered are also important.

In this study it is seen that that the proposed hybrid model RF-PSO is capable of predicting shear strength of undrained soil quickly with basic soil properties in a better way for use in the design of civil engineering structures. A limitation of this study is the number of samples tested from one of the highway projects of Vietnam. It would be better to use large/big data from other projects to confirm its wider applicability.

**Author Contributions:** Conceptualization, B.T.P., T.N.-T., N.A.-A., M.D.N., and I.P.; Data curation, M.D.N., H.D.N. and H.V.L.; Formal analysis, L.S.H., T.N.-T., N.A.-A., M.D.N., H.D.N., H.-B.L. and H.V.L.; Methodology, B.T.P., C.Q., N.A.-A. and H.-B.L.; Project administration, B.T.P. and T.N.-T.; Supervision, T.N.-T., N.A.-A. and I.P.; Validation, T.N.-T., N.A.-A., C.Q., and I.P.; Visualization, L.S.H. and C.Q.; Writing—original draft, all authors; Writing—review & editing, B.T.P., T.N.-T., N.A.-A., and I.P.; Funding: T.N.-T. and N.A.-A. All authors have read and agreed to the published version of the manuscript.

**Funding:** This research received no external funding.

**Conflicts of Interest:** The authors declare no conflict of interest.

## References


1. Poulos, H.G. Design of reinforcing piles to increase slope stability. *Can. Geotech. J.* **1995**, *32*, 808–818. [CrossRef]
2. Liu, Y.-J.; Wang, T.-W.; Cai, C.-F.; Li, Z.-X.; Cheng, D.-B. Effects of vegetation on runoff generation, sediment yield and soil shear strength on road-side slopes under a simulation rainfall test in the Three Gorges Reservoir Area, China. *Sci. Total Environ.* **2014**, *485*, 93–102. [CrossRef] [PubMed]
3. Hettiarachchi, H.; Brown, T. Use of SPT blow counts to estimate shear strength properties of soils: Energy balance approach. *J. Geotech. Geoenviron. Eng.* **2009**, *135*, 830–834. [CrossRef]
4. Motaghedi, H.; Eslami, A. Analytical approach for determination of soil shear strength parameters from CPT and CPTu data. *Arab. J. Sci. Eng.* **2014**, *39*, 4363–4376. [CrossRef]
5. Cha, M.; Cho, G.-C. Shear strength estimation of sandy soils using shear wave velocity. *Geotech. Test. J.* **2007**, *30*, 484–495.
6. Garven, E.; Vanapalli, S. Evaluation of empirical procedures for predicting the shear strength of unsaturated soils. In *Unsaturated Soils 2006, Fourth International Conference on Unsaturated Soils, Carefree, AZ, USA, 2–6 April 2006*; American Society of Civil Engineers: Reston, VA, USA, 2006; pp. 2570–2592.
7. Kim, B.-S.; Shibuya, S.; Park, S.-W.; Kato, S. Application of suction stress for estimating unsaturated shear strength of soils using direct shear testing under low confining pressure. *Can. Geotech. J.* **2010**, *47*, 955–970. [CrossRef]
8. Ohu, J.O.; Raghavan, G.; McKyes, E.; Mehuys, G. Shear strength prediction of compacted soils with varying added organic matter contents. *Trans. ASAE* **1986**, *29*, 351–355. [CrossRef]
9. Tiwari, B.; Marui, H. A new method for the correlation of residual shear strength of the soil with mineralogical composition. *J. Geotech. Geoenviron. Eng.* **2005**, *131*, 1139–1150. [CrossRef]
10. Vilar, O.M. A simplified procedure to estimate the shear strength envelope of unsaturated soils. *Can. Geotech. J.* **2006**, *43*, 1088–1095. [CrossRef]

11. Huang, B.; Qiu, M.; Lin, J.; Chen, J.; Jiang, F.; Wang, M.-K.; Ge, H.; Huang, Y. Correlation between shear strength and soil physicochemical properties of different weathering profiles of the non-eroded and collapsing gully soils in southern China. *J. Soils Sediments* **2019**, *19*, 3832–3846. [CrossRef]
12. Zhai, Q.; Rahardjo, H.; Satyanaga, A.; Dai, G. Estimation of unsaturated shear strength from soil–water characteristic curve. *Acta Geotech.* **2019**, *14*, 1977–1990. [CrossRef]
13. Leong, E.-C. Soil-water characteristic curves-Determination, estimation and application. *Jpn. Geotech. Soc. Spec. Publ.* **2019**, *7*, 21–30. [CrossRef]
14. Bui, D.T.; Nhu, V.-H.; Hoang, N.-D. Prediction of soil compression coefficient for urban housing project using novel integration machine learning approach of swarm intelligence and multi-layer perceptron neural network. *Adv. Eng. Inform.* **2018**, *38*, 593–604.
15. Chen, W.; Wang, Y.; Cao, G.; Chen, G.; Gu, Q. A random forest model based classification scheme for neonatal amplitude-integrated EEG. *Biomed. Eng. Online* **2014**, *13*, S4. [CrossRef]
16. Chou, J.-S.; Pham, A.-D. Enhanced artificial intelligence for ensemble approach to predicting high performance concrete compressive strength. *Constr. Build. Mater.* **2013**, *49*, 554–563. [CrossRef]
17. Koopialipoor, M.; Fallah, A.; Armaghani, D.J.; Azizi, A.; Mohamad, E.T. Three hybrid intelligent models in estimating flyrock distance resulting from blasting. *Eng. Comput.* **2019**, *35*, 243–256. [CrossRef]
18. Koopialipoor, M.; Ghaleini, E.N.; Tootoonchi, H.; Armaghani, D.J.; Haghighi, M.; Hedayat, A. Developing a new intelligent technique to predict overbreak in tunnels using an artificial bee colony-based ANN. *Environ. Earth Sci.* **2019**, *78*, 165. [CrossRef]
19. Pham, B.T.; Bui, D.T.; Prakash, I.; Dholakia, M. Hybrid integration of Multilayer Perceptron Neural Networks and machine learning ensembles for landslide susceptibility assessment at Himalayan area (India) using GIS. *Catena* **2017**, *149*, 52–63. [CrossRef]
20. Samui, P. Prediction of friction capacity of driven piles in clay using the support vector machine. *Can. Geotech. J.* **2008**, *45*, 288–295. [CrossRef]
21. Shahin, M.A.; Jaksa, M.B.; Maier, H.R. Recent advances and future challenges for artificial neural systems in geotechnical engineering applications. *Adv. Artif. Neural Syst.* **2009**, *2009*, 5. [CrossRef]
22. Dao, D.V.; Adeli, H.; Ly, H.-B.; Le, L.M.; Le, V.M.; Le, T.-T.; Pham, B.T. A Sensitivity and Robustness Analysis of GPR and ANN for High-Performance Concrete Compressive Strength Prediction Using a Monte Carlo Simulation. *Sustainability* **2020**, *12*, 830. [CrossRef]
23. Pham, B.T.; Avand, M.; Janizadeh, S.; Phong, T.V.; Al-Ansari, N.; Ho, L.S.; Das, S.; Le, H.V.; Amini, A.; Bozchaloei, S.K. GIS Based Hybrid Computational Approaches for Flash Flood Susceptibility Assessment. *Water* **2020**, *12*, 683. [CrossRef]
24. Pham, B.T.; Prakash, I.; Dou, J.; Singh, S.K.; Trinh, P.T.; Tran, H.T.; Le, T.M.; Van Phong, T.; Khoi, D.K.; Shirzadi, A. A novel hybrid approach of landslide susceptibility modelling using rotation forest ensemble and different base classifiers. *Geocarto Int.* **2019**, 1–25. [CrossRef]
25. Pham, B.T.; Bui, D.T.; Prakash, I.; Nguyen, L.H.; Dholakia, M. A comparative study of sequential minimal optimization-based support vector machines, vote feature intervals, and logistic regression in landslide susceptibility assessment using GIS. *Environ. Earth Sci.* **2017**, *76*, 371. [CrossRef]
26. Pham, B.T.; Bui, D.T.; Pham, H.V.; Le, H.Q.; Prakash, I.; Dholakia, M. Landslide hazard assessment using random subspace fuzzy rules based classifier ensemble and probability analysis of rainfall data: A case study at Mu Cang Chai District, Yen Bai Province (Viet Nam). *J. Indian Soc. Remote Sens.* **2017**, *45*, 673–683. [CrossRef]
27. Sharma, L.; Singh, R.; Umrao, R.; Sharma, K.; Singh, T. Evaluating the modulus of elasticity of soil using soft computing system. *Eng. Comput.* **2017**, *33*, 497–507. [CrossRef]
28. Kalkan, E.; Akbulut, S.; Tortum, A.; Celik, S. Prediction of the unconfined compressive strength of compacted granular soils by using inference systems. *Environ. Geol.* **2009**, *58*, 1429–1440. [CrossRef]
29. Nhu, V.H.; Hoang, N.D.; Duong, V.B.; Vu, H.D.; Bui, D.T. A hybrid computational intelligence approach for predicting soil shear strength for urban housing construction: a case study at Vinhomes Imperia project, Hai Phong City (Vietnam). *Eng. Comput.* **2019**, 1–14. [CrossRef]
30. Moavenian, M.; Nazem, M.; Carter, J.; Randolph, M. Numerical analysis of penetrometers free-falling into soil with shear strength increasing linearly with depth. *Comput. Geotech.* **2016**, *72*, 57–66. [CrossRef]
31. Pham, B.T.; Hoang, T.-A.; Nguyen, D.-M.; Bui, D.T. Prediction of shear strength of soft soil using machine learning methods. *Catena* **2018**, *166*, 181–191. [CrossRef]

32. Breiman, L. Random forests. *Mach. Learn.* **2001**, *45*, 5–32. [CrossRef]
33. Liaw, A.; Wiener, M. Classification and regression by randomForest. *R News* **2002**, *2*, 18–22.
34. Jahed Armaghani, D.; Hajihassani, M.; Yazdani Bejarbaneh, B.; Marto, A.; Tonnizam Mohamad, E. Indirect measure of shale shear strength parameters by means of rock index tests through an optimized artificial neural network. *Measurement* **2014**, *55*, 487–498. [CrossRef]
35. Hajihassani, M.; Armaghani, D.J.; Kalatehjari, R. Applications of particle swarm optimization in geotechnical engineering: a comprehensive review. *Geotech. Geol. Eng.* **2018**, *36*, 705–722. [CrossRef]
36. Hasanipanah, M.; Noorian-Bidgoli, M.; Armaghani, D.J.; Khamesi, H. Feasibility of PSO-ANN model for predicting surface settlement caused by tunneling. *Eng. Comput.* **2016**, *32*, 705–715. [CrossRef]
37. Kalatehjari, R.; Ali, N.; Kholghifard, M.; Hajihassani, M. The effects of method of generating circular slip surfaces on determining the critical slip surface by particle swarm optimization. *Arab. J. Geosci.* **2014**, *7*, 1529–1539. [CrossRef]
38. Das, B.M.; Sobhan, K. *Principles of Geotechnical Engineering*; Cengage Learning: Stamford, CT, USA, 2013.
39. Terzaghi, K.; Peck, R.B.; Mesri, G. *Soil Mechanics*; John Wiley & Sons: New York, NY, USA, 1996.
40. Hong, H.; Pourghasemi, H.R.; Pourtaghi, Z.S. Landslide susceptibility assessment in Lianhua County (China): a comparison between a random forest data mining technique and bivariate and multivariate statistical models. *Geomorphology* **2016**, *259*, 105–118. [CrossRef]
41. Stumpf, A.; Kerle, N. Object-oriented mapping of landslides using Random Forests. *Remote Sens. Environ.* **2011**, *115*, 2564–2577. [CrossRef]
42. Archer, K.J.; Kimes, R.V. Empirical characterization of random forest variable importance measures. *Comput. Stat. Data Anal.* **2008**, *52*, 2249–2260. [CrossRef]
43. Biau, G.; Devroye, L.; Lugosi, G. Consistency of random forests and other averaging classifiers. *J. Mach. Learn. Res.* **2008**, *9*, 2015–2033.
44. Trigila, A.; Iadanza, C.; Esposito, C.; Scarascia-Mugnozza, G. Comparison of Logistic Regression and Random Forests techniques for shallow landslide susceptibility assessment in Giampilieri (NE Sicily, Italy). *Geomorphology* **2015**, *249*, 119–136. [CrossRef]
45. Eberhart, R.; Kennedy, J. A new optimizer using particle swarm theory. In Proceedings of the MHS'95. Proceedings of the Sixth International Symposium on Micro Machine and Human Science, Nagoya, Japan, 4–6 October 1995; pp. 39–43.
46. Cheng, Y.; Li, L.; Chi, S.-C.; Wei, W. Particle swarm optimization algorithm for the location of the critical non-circular failure surface in two-dimensional slope stability analysis. *Comput. Geotech.* **2007**, *34*, 92–103. [CrossRef]
47. Awad, Z.K.; Aravinthan, T.; Zhuge, Y.; Gonzalez, F. A review of optimization techniques used in the design of fibre composite structures for civil engineering applications. *Mater. Des.* **2012**, *33*, 534–544. [CrossRef]
48. Chen, W.; Panahi, M.; Pourghasemi, H.R. Performance evaluation of GIS-based new ensemble data mining techniques of adaptive neuro-fuzzy inference system (ANFIS) with genetic algorithm (GA), differential evolution (DE), and particle swarm optimization (PSO) for landslide spatial modelling. *Catena* **2017**, *157*, 310–324. [CrossRef]
49. Qi, C.; Fourie, A.; Chen, Q.; Zhang, Q. A strength prediction model using artificial intelligence for recycling waste tailings as cemented paste backfill. *J. Clean. Prod.* **2018**, *183*, 566–578. [CrossRef]
50. Pedregosa, F.; Varoquaux, G.; Gramfort, A.; Michel, V.; Thirion, B.; Grisel, O.; Blondel, M.; Prettenhofer, P.; Weiss, R.; Dubourg, V. Scikit-learn: Machine learning in Python. *J. Mach. Learn. Res.* **2011**, *12*, 2825–2830.
51. Qi, C.; Chen, Q.; Fourie, A.; Zhang, Q. An intelligent modelling framework for mechanical properties of cemented paste backfill. *Miner. Eng.* **2018**, *123*, 16–27. [CrossRef]
52. Eberhart, R.C.; Shi, Y. Comparing inertia weights and constriction factors in particle swarm optimization. In Proceedings of the 2000 Congress on Evolutionary Computation, CEC00 (Cat. No.00TH8512), La Jolla, CA, USA, 16–19 July 2000; Volume 81, pp. 84–88.
53. Van den Bergh, F.; Engelbrecht, A.P. A study of particle swarm optimization particle trajectories. *Inf. Sci.* **2006**, *176*, 937–971. [CrossRef]
54. Li-ping, Z.; Huan-jun, Y.; Shang-xu, H. Optimal choice of parameters for particle swarm optimization. *J. Zhejiang Univ. Sci. A* **2005**, *6*, 528–534. [CrossRef]
55. Qi, C.; Fourie, A.; Chen, Q.; Tang, X.; Zhang, Q.; Gao, R. Data-driven modelling of the flocculation process on mineral processing tailings treatment. *J. Clean. Prod.* **2018**, *196*, 505–516. [CrossRef]

56. Qi, C.; Ly, H.-B.; Chen, Q.; Le, T.-T.; Le, V.M.; Pham, B.T. Flocculation-dewatering prediction of fine mineral tailings using a hybrid machine learning approach. *Chemosphere* **2020**, *244*, 125450. [CrossRef] [PubMed]
57. Pham, B.T.; Le, L.M.; Le, T.-T.; Bui, K.-T.T.; Le, V.M.; Ly, H.-B.; Prakash, I. Development of advanced artificial intelligence models for daily rainfall prediction. *Atmos. Res.* **2020**, *237*, 104845. [CrossRef]
58. Dao, D.V.; Ly, H.-B.; Vu, H.-L.T.; Le, T.-T.; Pham, B.T. Investigation and Optimization of the C-ANN Structure in Predicting the Compressive Strength of Foamed Concrete. *Materials* **2020**, *13*, 1072. [CrossRef] [PubMed]
59. Van Dao, D.; Jaafari, A.; Bayat, M.; Mafi-Gholami, D.; Qi, C.; Moayedi, H.; Van Phong, T.; Ly, H.-B.; Le, T.-T.; Trinh, P.T. A spatially explicit deep learning neural network model for the prediction of landslide susceptibility. *Catena* **2020**, *188*, 104451.
60. Pham, B.T.; Phong, T.V.; Nguyen, H.D.; Qi, C.; Al-Ansari, N.; Amini, A.; Ho, L.S.; Tuyen, T.T.; Yen, H.P.H.; Ly, H.-B. A Comparative Study of Kernel Logistic Regression, Radial Basis Function Classifier, Multinomial Naïve Bayes, and Logistic Model Tree for Flash Flood Susceptibility Mapping. *Water* **2020**, *12*, 239. [CrossRef]
61. Nguyen, V.V.; Pham, B.T.; Vu, B.T.; Prakash, I.; Jha, S.; Shahabi, H.; Shirzadi, A.; Ba, D.N.; Kumar, R.; Chatterjee, J.M. Hybrid machine learning approaches for landslide susceptibility modeling. *Forests* **2019**, *10*, 157. [CrossRef]
62. Nguyen, M.D.; Pham, B.T.; Tuyen, T.T.; Yen, H.; Phan, H.; Prakash, I.; Vu, T.T.; Chapi, K.; Shirzadi, A.; Shahabi, H. Development of an Artificial Intelligence Approach for Prediction of Consolidation Coefficient of Soft Soil: A Sensitivity Analysis. *Open Constr. Build. Technol. J.* **2019**, *13*, 178–188. [CrossRef]
63. Dao, D.V.; Ly, H.-B.; Trinh, S.H.; Le, T.-T.; Pham, B.T. Artificial intelligence approaches for prediction of compressive strength of geopolymer concrete. *Materials* **2019**, *12*, 983. [CrossRef]
64. Dao, D.V.; Trinh, S.H.; Ly, H.-B.; Pham, B.T. Prediction of compressive strength of geopolymer concrete using entirely steel slag aggregates: Novel hybrid artificial intelligence approaches. *Appl. Sci.* **2019**, *9*, 1113. [CrossRef]
65. Pham, B.T.; Nguyen, M.D.; Van Dao, D.; Prakash, I.; Ly, H.-B.; Le, T.-T.; Ho, L.S.; Nguyen, K.T.; Ngo, T.Q.; Hoang, V. Development of artificial intelligence models for the prediction of Compression Coefficient of soil: An application of Monte Carlo sensitivity analysis. *Sci. Total Environ.* **2019**, *679*, 172–184. [CrossRef]
66. Nguyen, H.-L.; Pham, B.T.; Son, L.H.; Thang, N.T.; Ly, H.-B.; Le, T.-T.; Ho, L.S.; Le, T.-H.; Tien Bui, D. Adaptive network based fuzzy inference system with meta-heuristic optimizations for international roughness index prediction. *Appl. Sci.* **2019**, *9*, 4715. [CrossRef]
67. Janizadeh, S.; Avand, M.; Jaafari, A.; Phong, T.V.; Bayat, M.; Ahmadisharaf, E.; Prakash, I.; Pham, B.T.; Lee, S. Prediction Success of Machine Learning Methods for Flash Flood Susceptibility Mapping in the Tafresh Watershed, Iran. *Sustainability* **2019**, *11*, 5426. [CrossRef]
68. Kohestani, V.; Hassanlourad, M.; Ardakani, A. Evaluation of liquefaction potential based on CPT data using random forest. *Nat. Hazards* **2015**, *79*, 1079–1089. [CrossRef]
69. Wan, S. Entropy-based particle swarm optimization with clustering analysis on landslide susceptibility mapping. *Environ. Earth Sci.* **2012**, *68*. [CrossRef]
70. Qi, C.; Fourie, A.; Chen, Q. Neural network and particle swarm optimization for predicting the unconfined compressive strength of cemented paste backfill. *Constr. Build. Mater.* **2018**, *159*, 473–478. [CrossRef]
71. Pham, B.T.; Nguyen, M.D.; Bui, K.-T.T.; Prakash, I.; Chapi, K.; Bui, D.T. A novel artificial intelligence approach based on Multi-layer Perceptron Neural Network and Biogeography-based Optimization for predicting coefficient of consolidation of soil. *Catena* **2019**, *173*, 302–311. [CrossRef]

*Article*

# Landslide Risk Mapping in an Urban Area of the City of Natal, Brazil

**Laddyla Bezerra [1,*], Osvaldo de Freitas Neto [1], Olavo Santos, Jr. [1] and Slobodan Mickovski [2]**

1 Graduate Program in Civil Engineering (PEC-UFRN), Federal University of Rio Grande do Norte, Campus Universitário, Natal, RN 59078-970, Brazil; osvaldocivil@ufrn.edu.br (O.d.F.N.); olavo.santos@ufrn.edu.br (O.S.J.)

2 Department of Civil Engineering and Environment, School of Computing, Engineering and Built Environment, Glasgow Caledonian University, Glasgow G4 0BA, UK; slobodan.mickovski@gcu.ac.uk

* Correspondence: laddyla@ufrn.edu.br; Tel.: +55-84996943343

Received: 17 September 2020; Accepted: 16 November 2020; Published: 18 November 2020

**Abstract:** Landslides are part of the natural processes of Earth's surface dynamic, which could be accelerated or triggered by anthropic interference. Inadequate occupation of areas highly susceptible to landslide processes is the principal cause of accidents on Brazilian urban slopes, especially those occupied by settlements and slums. In Natal, Rio Grande do Norte state, Brazil, the existence of areas with steep and densely occupied slopes makes the municipality susceptible to landslides. In this context, the present study aimed to map the risk of landslides in an urban area located in the city of Natal. Using the quali-quantitative model proposed by Faria (2011), adapted for the conditions of the study area, which applies a multicriteria analytical hierarchy process (AHP) to a Geographic Information System (GIS), 11 risk indicators were submitted to pairwise comparisons by 10 risk management specialists in order to determine the relative importance (weighting) for each of these factors as a function of their contribution to the risk. The weightings obtained were combined to produce the final risk map of the study area, using a map algebra framework. The results show the existence of a critical risk for the resident population, primarily related to the possibility of a landslide, with potentially negative economic, environmental, and mainly social impacts.

**Keywords:** risk; hazard; vulnerability; landslides; multicriteria assessment; analytical hierarchy process

## 1. Introduction

In recent decades, there has been a considerable increase in the frequency, intensity, and impacts generated by socioenvironmental disasters worldwide [1]. According to the World Disaster Report 2010, with a focus on urban risks, 4014 natural disasters occurred around the world between 2000 and 2009, affecting more than one million people. In Brazil, a report prepared by [2] revealed that 22% of the socioenvironmental disasters recorded between 1991 and 2012 occurred in the 1990s, 56% between 2000 and 2009, and 22% in just three years (between 2010 and 2012). The document also indicates an increase in the number of disasters associated with landslides between 1990 and 2000. According to [3], this significant increase in the number of landslides on Brazilian slopes is caused primarily by the lack of urban planning and infrastructure. The latter fact has led the most underprivileged individuals to occupy naturally unsuitable areas or those that are highly susceptible to unstable slopes, mostly as a result of the low real estate value of the land.

Unsuitable occupation of areas susceptible to landslides in the city of Natal, Brazil, has made them vulnerable to slope instability. In 2014, two great magnitude natural disasters associated with intensity of rainfall were recorded in the districts of Mãe Luiza and Rocas, within Natal. The accidents were characterized, respectively, as sand flow on dune area and failure of the soil nail wall on Barreiras Formation sediment [4]. Both events had significant social and environmental impacts. To mitigate or even prevent future socioenvironmental disasters similar to those described above from happening, new research projects dedicated to the study of risk areas are needed.

Risk analysis can be carried out either through a qualitative, quali-quantitative or quantitative approach [5]. Risk mapping in Brazil and many other countries predominantly uses qualitative methodologies [6]. This type of assessment is based on professional judgement via field observations, interpretation of aerial photographs, and information supplied by residents of the region under study. Many researchers believe that this leads to a certain subjectivity in the results obtained [7]. The outputs of quantitative methods, in turn, are numerical estimations, namely, the probability of occurrence of landslides and the probability distribution of consequences within a certain area. However, applications are restricted to localized studies in limited areas, by the necessity of a large volume of detailed data on the slopes, acquired with laboratory tests and field measurements. In the quali-quantitative methods, assessments consider that a number of factors influence stability. The scores attributed to each of these factors are used to evaluate how favorable or unfavorable they are to the occurrence of instability [8]. The last decade has seen an evolution of quali-quantitative analyses with a view to improve qualitative risk mapping. These reduce subjectivity, thereby increasing the hierarchization and prioritization of risk sectors. Ref. [9] proposed a quali-quantitative methodology based on the Analytical Hierarchy Process (AHP). The application of the AHP method in risk mapping makes the process more systematic and less subjective. The sensibility analyses used in the method allow for a higher perception of effectiveness in qualitative assessment and, as a result, a higher confidence level in decision-making [10].

The aim of the present study is to apply an adapted version of the methodology proposed by [9] in order to diagnose the occurrence of landslides in an area near the São José do Jacó settlement, in the city of Natal. The methodology used to achieve this aim was a multicriteria decision-making technique (AHP) and Geographic Information System (GIS) system for application at the local level. This approach includes the use of a limited number of key risk indicators and allows the delineation and mapping of risk zones with different associated risk levels which can help engineers and land planners to design and assess infrastructure and evaluate its effects on the surrounding environment.

## 2. Materials and Methods

### 2.1. Quali-Quantitative Risk Assessment Model Proposed by Faria (2011)

The AHP, developed by Saaty in the 1970s, proposes a method that could represent a decision-making process. The aim was to reach better conclusions based on a hierarchy, pairwise comparisons, judgement scales, weight and criterion attribution, and selection of the best alternatives for a finite number of variables [11]. Ref. [9] applied the multicriteria decision-making tool AHP to the risk mapping qualitative methodology adopted by [12]. This procedure gave rise to a hybrid methodology classified as quali-quantitative. The application of this approach includes three main stages: structuring, comparative judgements, and synthesis of priorities. These stages, as presented by [10], are shown on Figure 1.

The first step of the process involves deconstructing the problem into a hierarchical framework, organized by levels, with the problem-solving objective at the top and criteria to be assessed and their relevant alternatives in the decision process at the lower levels [13]. Figure 2 illustrates this stage.

In the comparative judgements stage, risk assessment specialists make a pairwise comparison between the criteria and alternatives to determine the relative importance (weighting) of each criterion. To this end, a number scale is needed to indicate how many times one element is more important than another, and the Saaty Fundamental Scale [13,14] can be used for this purpose.

Finally, in the synthesis of priorities phase, the AHP calculates all the weightings of the hierarchical levels. The pairwise comparison matrix created is submitted to the eigenvector mathematical technique. Beforehand, they undergo sensitivity analysis to assess the coherence of the specialists' judgements.

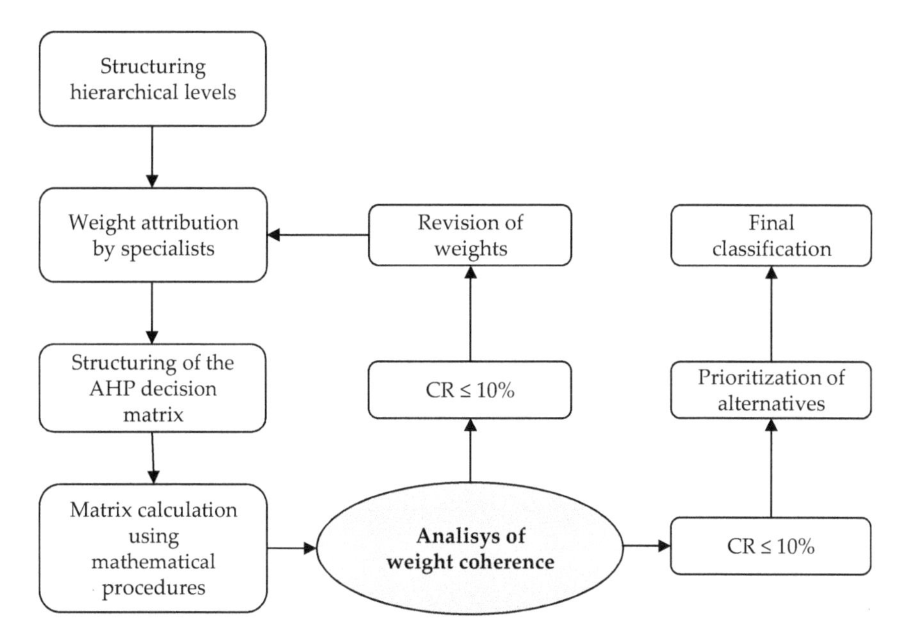


**Figure 1.** The main stages of the analytical hierarchy process (AHP) method. Adapted from [10].

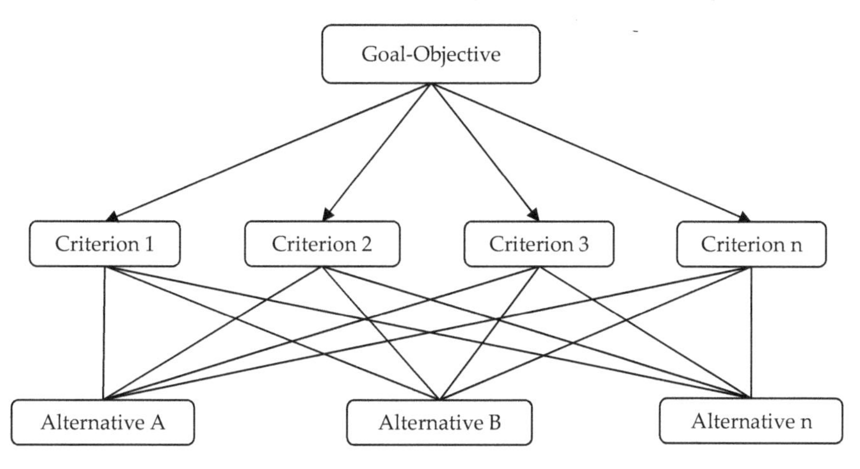


**Figure 2.** Example of the modeling or hierarchical structuring stage. Adapted from [13].

Ref. [15] recommend calculating the Consistency Ratio (CR), whose limit value at which judgements are considered inconsistent is 10%. For CRs above the reference value, Ref. [15] suggests that the problem be studied and the attributed weightings be revised. The CR calculation procedure involves estimating the maximum eigenvalue ($\lambda_{max}$) and consistency index (CI), as described by [15].

## 2.2. Research Methodology

The risk mapping for the present study was based on an adapted version of the quali-quantitative approach described by [9]. The adaptation mentioned occurred in the selection phase of socioenvironmental indicators, with the purpose of adapting the methodology to the specificities of the study area, as well as to the history of landslides known in the region of the municipality of Natal.

The application of the proposed methodology considered 11 socioenvironmental indicators assessed as decisive in triggering landslides at the site, which were evaluated and characterized through technical inspection in homes, information provided by residents, aerial photography, and produced thematic maps. Figure 3 illustrates the indicators adopted in the study.

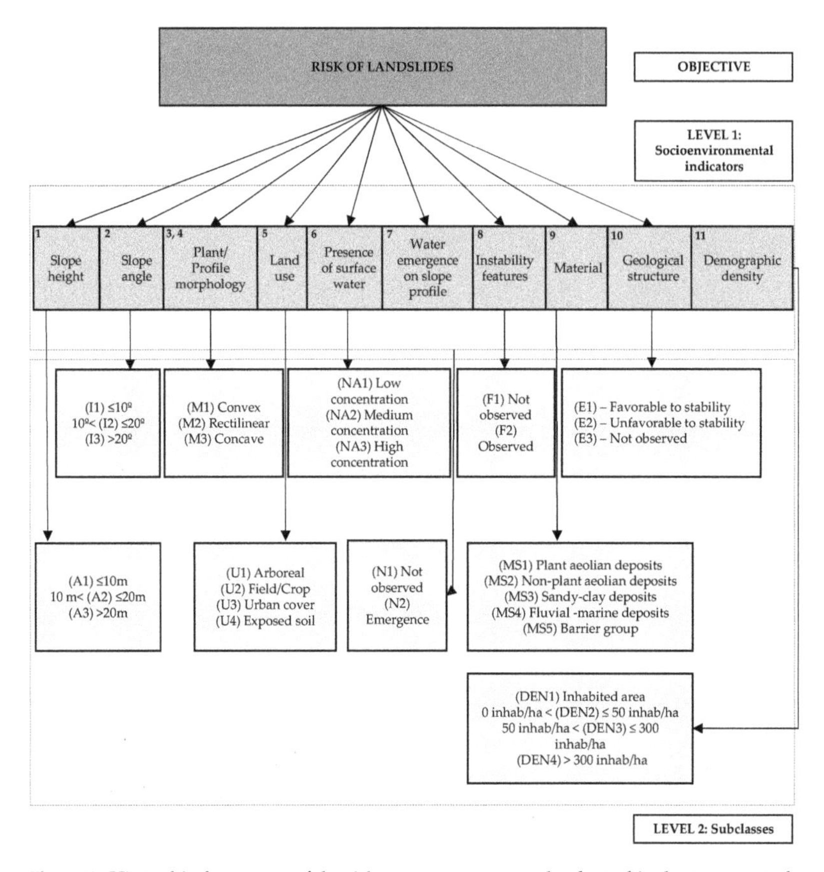


**Figure 3.** Hierarchical structure of the risk assessment approach adopted in the present study.

In choosing these socioenvironmental indicators, we sought to consider the natural and anthropic factors that affect slope stability. In terms of the former, the amplitude, inclination, slope morphology in plan and profile, geological structure, and substrate material were considered. With respect to anthropic factors, processes that produce unfavorable changes to slope stability were considered. Anthropic processes cause changes in the state of stress and affect the shear strength of materials. These processes include land use, the presence of water on the surface, and water arising from the slope profile.

The indicator "presence of instability features" is considered as a key criterion in mapping the risk of landslides to provide indications of their occurrence or imminence on the slope. This criterion was adopted in the analysis since there is evidence of a creeping process in triggering landslides at the study site.

In order to observe instability features, inspections were made at 62 points on the slope in the study area, encompassing residences and the surface area of the slope, in addition to information contained in the occurrence registries provided by the Municipal Civil Defense.

Field inspections sought to identify information that can indicate the occurrence or the possibility of developing landslides in the area or the possibility of their occurring at the site, such as the existence of cracks in the floor and/or masonry, the inclination of rigid structures, such as retaining walls, large trees, fences, posts, and the facade of residences and subsidence of the residential floor, among other problems.

Vulnerability, as well as hazards, is an important component in risk assessment. It reflects the interaction between potentially harmful phenomena and the elements exposed to risk. Demographic density was adopted in this study as an assessment criterion of the population's exposure to the risk of landslides in the study area.

The degree of importance for each socioenvironmental indicator in risk generation was measured using the weights of the AHP method. The authors assigned these weights in collaboration with ten professionals who were not involved in the research, with a background in geological-geotechnical risk mapping, consisting of seven civil engineers, two geologists, and one geographer, 6 of whom were university professors and 4 were employed by private companies.

In order to facilitate obtaining weights by consulting specialists, they received a base document consisting of a text file and Excel spreadsheet. The document consisted of a brief presentation of the AHP technique using an explanatory text, presenting the risk indicators selected for analysis, in addition to a guide on how the electronic spreadsheet should be filled out.

After the specialists attributed the weights, the Consistency Ratio (CR) was used to analyze the consistency of the weights obtained. The specialists' assessments were considered acceptable when the CR was less than or equal to 10%.

For the spatial implementation of the risk map (using geographic information system (GIS) software), explained in Figure 4, each criterion/indicator ($C_i$) was transformed into a thematic map in raster format and reclassified as a function of preliminarily established subclasses. This operation intended to transform input raster cell values to the desired output values and enable linear standardization of attributes that exhibit different valuations [8].

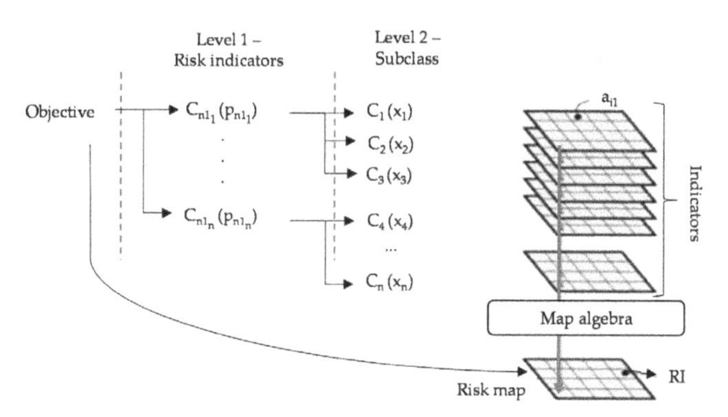


**Figure 4.** Schematic procedure for spatial implementation of the risk map in commercial software. Adapted from [8].

As shown in Figure 4, the criteria that influence reaching the objective (landslide risk map) were deconstructed into two hierarchical levels. Level 1 criteria ($C_{n1}$) are the risk indicators (slope height, slope angle, etc.) and level 2 ($C_{n2}$) are their respective subclasses. Each criterion in both levels was attributed an AHP weight ($p_n$ and $x_n$ for levels 1 and 2, respectively).

The spatial performance ($a_i$) of each cell of the mapped area was calculated by multiplying indicator weightings by the weighting of the class of the respective indicator, obtaining the risk indicator, as demonstrated in Equation (1), where $p$ is the weighting of the risk indicator and x is the weighting of the class of the respective risk indicator (subcriterion).

$$\mathrm{RI} = \sum_{i=1}^{n} p_i x_i / 100 \quad (1)$$

The final risk classification was reached using a statistical-based slicing method [9], denominated here as degree of risk (DR). According to this procedure, the risk indicator for each pixel should be compared to the arithmetic mean ($\mu_{IR}$) of the risk index for all pixels, added or subtracted by half the standard deviation ($\sigma$), as shown in Table 1.

**Table 1.** Criteria adopted to classify degree of risk (DR). Modified from Faria (2011).

| Risk Index (RI) | (DR) |
|---|---|
| $\mathrm{RI} < \mu_{\mathrm{RI}} - \frac{1}{2}\sigma$ | Low |
| $\mu_{\mathrm{RI}} - \frac{1}{2}\sigma \leq \mathrm{RI} \leq \mu_{\mathrm{RI}} + \frac{1}{2}\sigma$ | Medium |
| $\mathrm{RI} > \mu_{\mathrm{IRI}} + \frac{1}{2}\sigma$ | High |

### 2.3. *Site Description*

The study area in this work is a settlement of informal origin, located at an urban hill between the Rocas and Praia do Meio neighborhoods, in the city of Natal, Rio Grande do Norte state, Brazil (Figure 5).

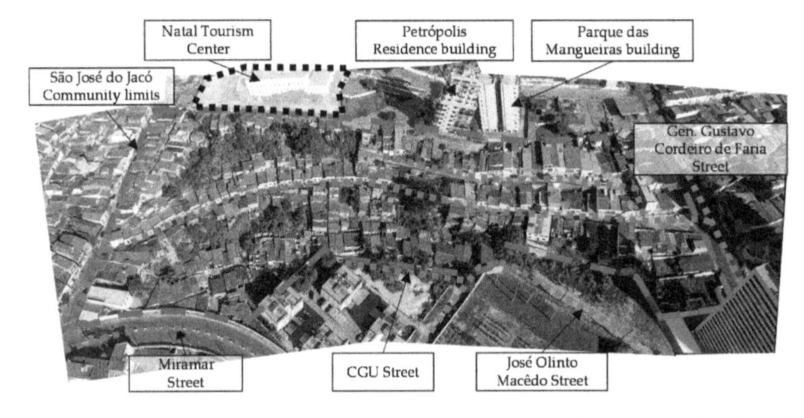


**Figure 5.** Aerial photograph of the São José do Jacó Community, with main streets highlighted.

The city of Natal was built in an area characterized by dune fields formed by aeolian sediments, next to the beach line—coastal trays entering the continent. The urban fabric of Natal area is, almost entirely, atop the coastal trays, which, in geological terms, correspond to the Barreiras Formation and Potengi Formation, lithological units formed by sediments of tertiary and quaternary age, in which layers of clay sands, pure sands, and silty sands are interspersed. There are also occurrences of conglomeratic layers and other strongly cemented layers.

The analyzed sector involves a 3.18 ha area and approximately 240 homes and 600 residents, according to data from the 2010 Brazil Demographic Census. The municipal macro zoning plan locates the region in a densified area and it is considered a Special Area of Social Interest Type 1—Slum [16]. Around half of the area of Rocas lies on a predominately a flat terrain, with an altitude of 5 m above sea level (a.s.l.), with few points where the altitude exceeds 15 m a.s.l. The highest elevations, in the limit region between Rocas and Praia do Meio, are occupied by the São José do Jacó Community, where the altitudes vary between 7m and 37m a.s.l. and the slopes between 10° and 20°.

The region under study has a history of slope instability. In June 2014, part of the 13m high retaining structure failed and collapsed after around 50 h of steady rain, totaling 315 mm. The cause of the failure is primarily associated to the lack of an efficient drainage system in the structure. Figure 6 shows photographs of the collapsed retaining structure in the community of São José do Jacó.

**Figure 6.** Area affected by the collapse of a retaining structure in the community of São José do Jacó.

In addition to this large disaster, evidence of the movement in the form of tilted trees, retaining structures and the facades of dwellings, denotes the presence of creep in full development in the community of São José do Jacó.

## 3. Results and Discussion

### 3.1. *Weightings Obtained by the AHP Method*

Table 2 shows pairwise comparisons, expressed by the weightings obtained for the risk indicators and their classes. These weightings represent the order of importance of each risk indicator in the occurrence of landslides processes on the urban slope occupied in the study area. Table 3 shows a summary of the sensitivity analysis for the risk indicator matrix.

**Table 2.** Weightings obtained for the risk indicators and their classes.

| Risk Indicators | Weights (%) | Classes | Weights (%) |
|---|---|---|---|
| Slope height | 3.21% | $H \leq 10$ m | 8.82% |
| | | 10 m $< H <$ 20 m | 24.31% |
| | | $H \geq 20$ m | 66.87% |
| Slope angle | 5.79% | $A \leq 10°$ | 8.33% |
| | | $10° < A < 20°$ | 19.32% |
| | | $A \geq 20°$ | 72.35% |
| Plant morphology | 2.11% | Convex | 12.01% |
| | | Rectilinear | 13.43% |
| | | Concave | 74.56% |
| Profile morphology | 2.15% | Convex | 20.00% |
| | | Rectilinear | 20.00% |
| | | Concave | 60.00% |
| Land use/cover | 8.63% | Arboreal | 6.38% |
| | | Field/crop | 6.71% |
| | | Urban cover | 30.77% |
| | | Exposed soil | 56.15% |
| Presence of surface water | 2.22% | None/Low concentration | 10.62% |
| | | Medium concentration | 26.05% |
| | | High concentration/Seepage line visible | 63.33% |

**Table 2.** *Cont.*

| Risk Indicators | Weights (%) | Classes | Weights (%) |
|---|---|---|---|
| Water emergence in the hillside profile | 11.69% | Observed<br>Not observed | 87.50%<br>12.50% |
| Instability features | 19.90% | Observed<br>Not observed | 87.50%<br>12.50% |
| Substrate material | 11.51% | Coastal plant eolian deposits<br>Coastal non-plant eolian deposits<br>Sandy and sandy-clay deposits<br>Fluvial-marine deposits<br>Barrier group | 7.39%<br>46.56%<br>19.58%<br>14.42%<br>12.06% |
| Geological structure | 12.16% | Favorable to stability<br>Unfavorable<br>Not observed | 8.82%<br>66.87%<br>24.31% |
| Demographic density | 20.64% | Inhabited area<br>0 inhab/ha < (DEN) ≤ 50 inhab/hectare<br>50 inhab/ha < (DEN) ≤ 300 inhab/hectare<br>(DEN) > 300 inhab/hectare | 4.17%<br>13.30%<br>26.76%<br>55.77% |

**Table 3.** Sensitivity analysis of reciprocal matrix risk indicators.

| Sensitivity Analysis | |
|---|---|
| Matrix order | 11.00 |
| $\lambda_{max}$ [1] | 12.09 |
| CI [2] | 0.1086 |
| CR [3] | 7.10% |

[1] $\lambda_{max}$: Maximum eigenvalue; [2] CI: Consistency Index; [3] CR: Consistency Ratio.

The Consistency Ratio (CR) was less than 10% for the risk indicator matrix, as recommended by the AHP methodology. This value indicates an acceptable consistency level in the comparisons performed.

Two other indications of reliability in the specialists' judgements are a CI near zero and $\lambda_{max}$ value near the order of the comparison matrix. The latter derives from the corollary adopted in the AHP method developed by [17] and considers that a reciprocal matrix A, with positive input values only consistent if $\lambda_{max} = n$.

### 3.2. *Risk Mapping*

Given the two elements essential to risk formulation—the hazard and the vulnerability—distinct products were created for each of these elements and combined following the national and international trend to produce the risk map. Figure 7 illustrates the process of obtaining intermediate maps and the risk map.

#### 3.2.1. Hazard Map

The hazard map created using the AHP method (Figure 8) showed that most of the study area (48%) lies in a high-hazard zone for the occurrence of landslides, 45.3% is in the low-hazard category, and only 6.7% is considered a medium hazard.

To establish a correlation between spatialization of the hazard classes obtained for the slope and each of the indicators assessed, the contribution of the natural physical traits of the area was analyzed separately from contributions of anthropic factors using a susceptibility map (Figure 9).

Of the six parameters used to create the susceptibility map (slope height, slope angle, plant and profile morphology, substrate material, and geological structure), the slope angle was the factor that influenced spatialization the most, primarily due to the weighting attributed to it by the AHP method.

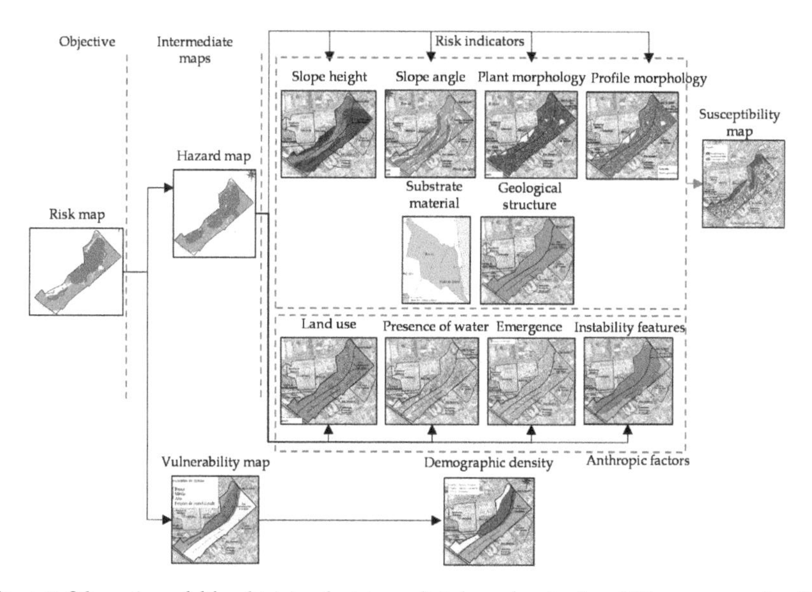


**Figure 7.** Schematic model for obtaining the intermediate hazard and vulnerability maps as well as the risk map for the study area.

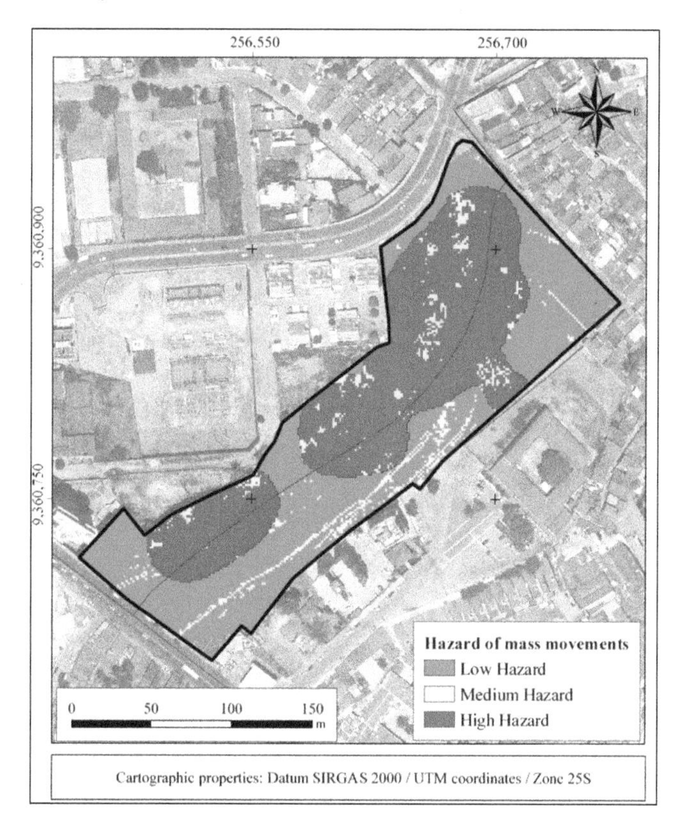


**Figure 8.** Landslide hazard map produced for the study area.

The analysis of the contribution of anthropogenic factors (land use/cover, presence of surface water, water emergence on the hillside profile, and instability features) shows that the presence of instability features governed the spatial arrangement of hazard classes, raising it to the "high" category in areas where scars were observed—i.e., signs of previous slope failure were visible.

Comparison between the results of the susceptibility and hazard maps, in which anthropic action was included, revealed that if only the natural physical traits were analyzed, the study area would not be highly susceptible to landslides. However, anthropogenic use and occupation of the slope is the main factor that poses hazard to the resident population, making it hazardous for human occupation. Thus, since the region under study is an occupied slope, it is important that public entities monitor it in order to prevent loss of life and property.

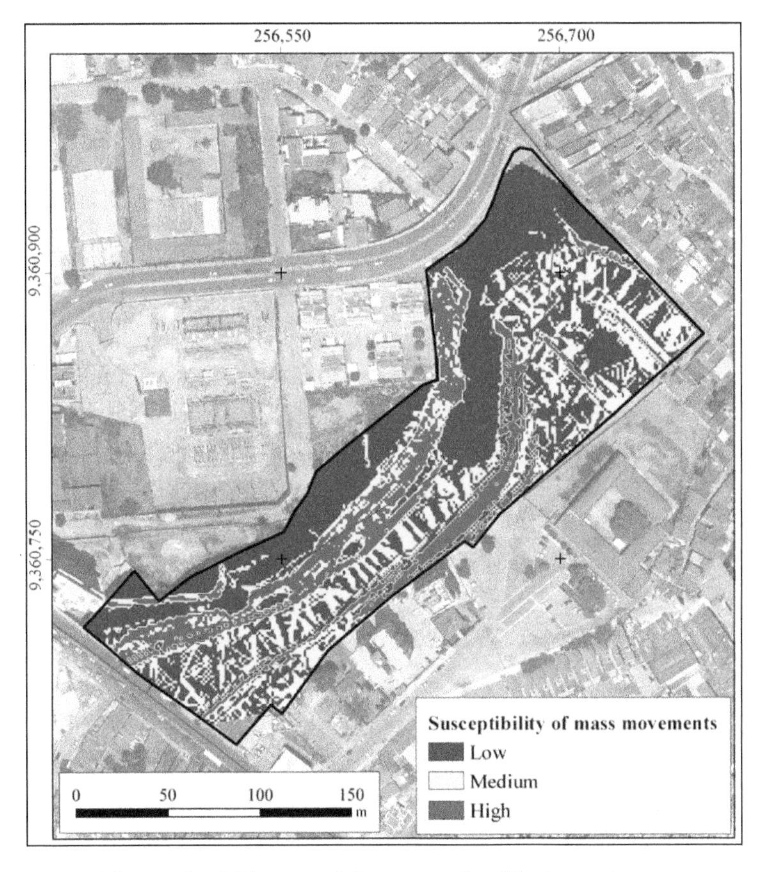


**Figure 9.** Landslide susceptibility map produced for the study area.

### 3.2.2. Vulnerability Map

The vulnerability map produced by a procedure similar to that described for risk is presented in Figure 10. A large part of the study area exhibited medium (50.97%) to high (32.01%) vulnerability, generally associated with a significant number of residential plots occupied by substandard housing and high population density, located on sloping terrain that would require more appropriate building techniques, and more space between residences.

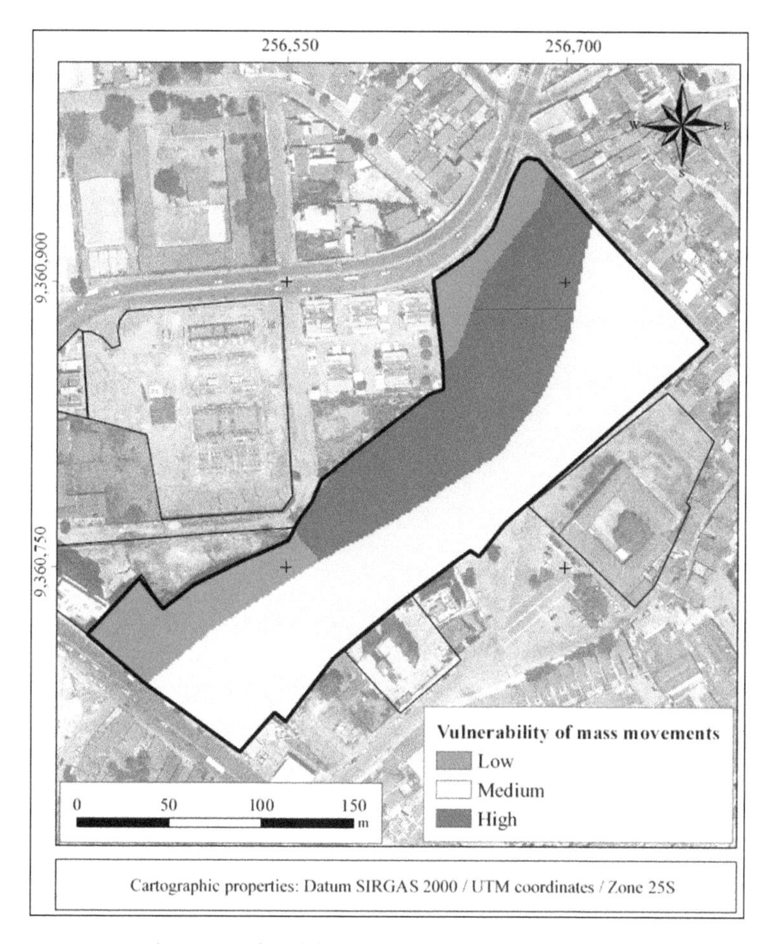


**Figure 10.** Vulnerability map produced for the study area.

Despite the fact that the financial status of the population that inhabit the study area was not considered in the weighting attribution phase of the AHP method, it is important to include it in vulnerability analysis, given that this trait affects how residents deal with socioenvironmental disasters such as landslides. There is a general agreement that households with higher income tend to have better built homes and are thereby better equipped to withstand extreme natural events.

Based on this hypothesis, assessment of income distribution, obtained from [18] shows that 50% of the private dwellings in the study area are occupied by low-income families, that is, those earning up to one-half the minimum monthly wage (≈USD 125.00).

It is important to observe, therefore, that the sector with more disadvantaged families—that is, in poverty or extreme poverty—contains the highest demographic density (more than 300 inhabitants per hectare). In addition to having greater difficulty in evacuating the population in the event of a disaster in this region, the inhabitants are also more vulnerable due to the infrastructure characteristics of their dwellings and the surrounding area.

### 3.2.3. Risk Map

The final element of the mapping process is illustrated in Figure 11.

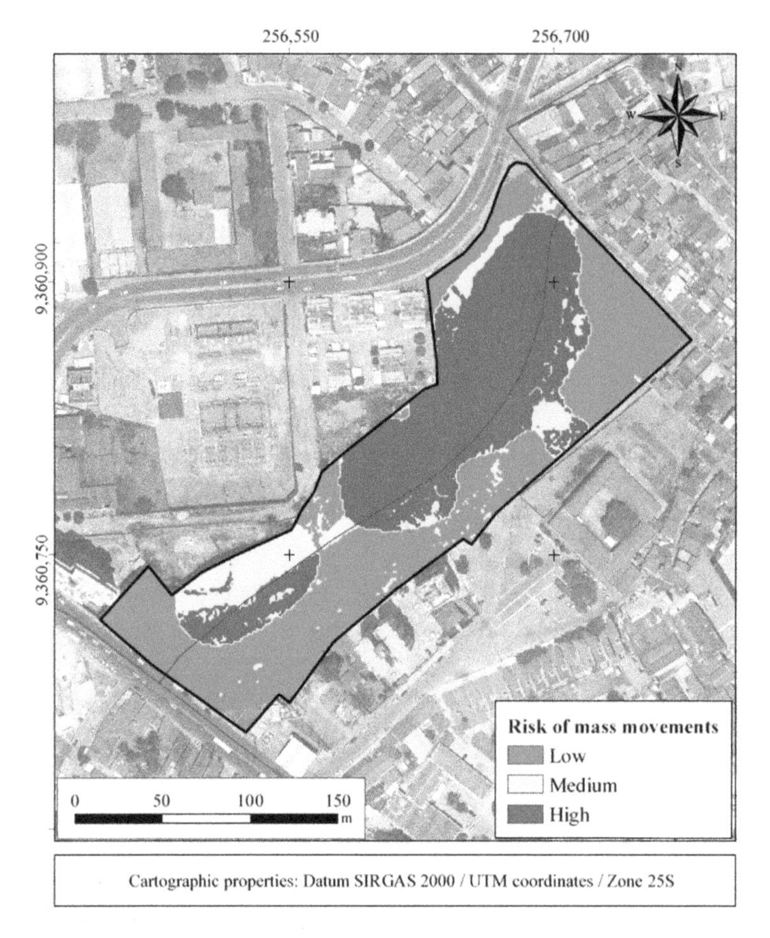


**Figure 11.** Risk map of the study area.

Risk mapping shows that the area exhibits a degree of slope instability risk ranging from low to high. The low-risk category accounted for 46% of the total area, followed by the high-risk (41%) and medium-risk groups (13%), which represents about 600 people under risk of landslides in an area of approximately 3.2 ha.

In general, the low-risk areas were concentrated mainly on Altamira Street and the first portion of Desembargador Lins Bahia Street (Figure 12), and exhibited geomorphological conditions that display low landslide potential, with a slope height below 20 m, low slope angle (less than 10°), convex/divergent plant morphology, and rectilinear and/or convex profile morphology.

With respect to the contribution of anthropic interferences in these areas, there is an absence or reduction in instability, no water on the slope surface or emergence points along the slope profile, which may be related to the existence, albeit incipient, of sewer, water supply, and rainwater drainage systems. In addition, these lower risk areas are characterized by low and medium vulnerability, due to a lower demographic density and households with higher incomes when compared to medium or high-risk regions, which exhibit a direct relation with better infrastructure and consequently with the response to a landslide.

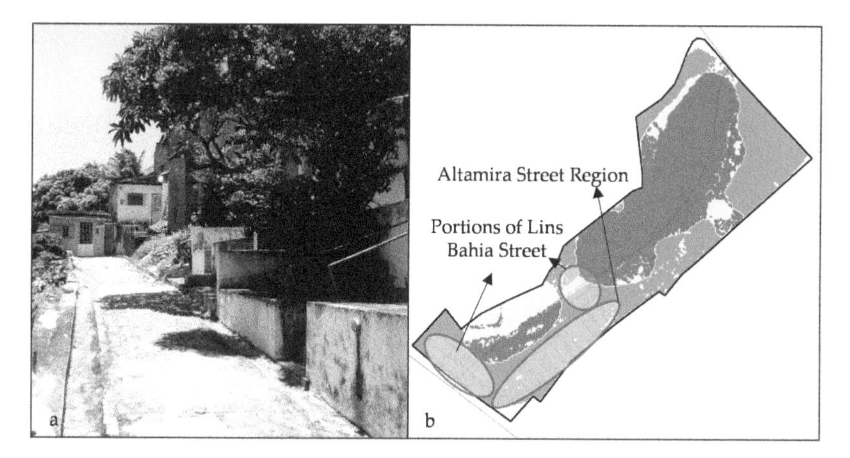


**Figure 12.** Low-risk regions identified in the assessment: photo of Altamira Street (**a**) with the surrounding area highlighted in (**b**).

In the slope regions classified as medium risk, the greatest contribution to obtaining this degree was the type of anthropic interference on the slope and the influence of vulnerability. The unfavorable contribution of human interventions in the area is evident on Desembargador Lins Bahia Street, where the risk of landslides rose from low to high (Figure 13a) due to the rupture of a retaining structure, which caused the emergence of instability features, which are extremely important in the analysis of hazard and risk.

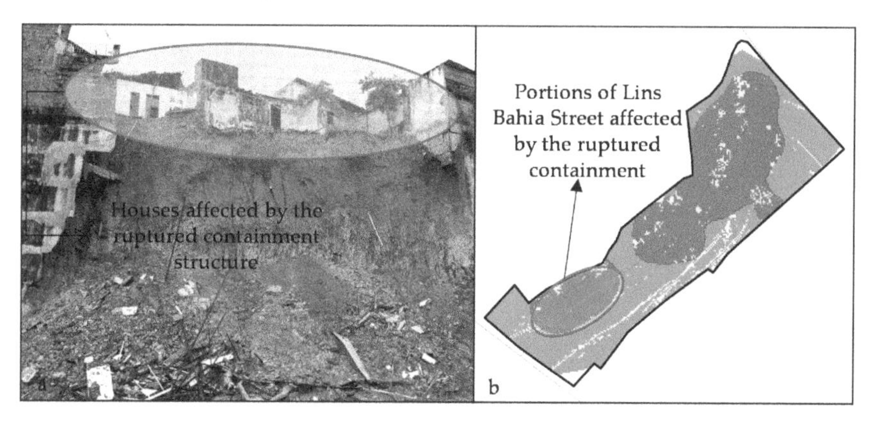


**Figure 13.** Unfavorable contribution of human interventions in the area near the containment curtain in obtaining medium risk: (**a**) portion of Lins Bahia Street with high risk; (**b**) houses affected by the ruptured containment structure.

In high-risk areas, nearly 50% of the region analyzed, the geological conditions exhibited a greater potential of developing landslides, with slope height values between 10 and 20 m and higher than 20 m, a high slope angle (more than 20°), predominantly convergent plant morphology, concave slope profile, and areas with little or no plant cover and even impermeable surfaces. In relation to the anthropic interventions on the slope, field visits revealed a large number of haphazard cuts. These cuts were made to allow construction of access roads to dwellings located at the top, foot, and slope of the hillside. Figure 14 illustrates this situation.

**Figure 14.** Construction of homes halfway up the slope.

Human action in the area is also reflected in the disposal of waste and rubble on the slope (Figure 15). According to [19], these materials are heterogeneous and geotechnically quite unstable. Waste deposition increases the weight on the slope and contributes to the triggering of landslides.

**Figure 15.** Waste and rubble deposition on the hillside within the site area.

Leaks in water supply and sewer pipes were also observed within the site area (Figure 16a,b). Furthermore, despite the installation of a sanitary sewer in 2014, many residents of high-risk areas continue to use septic tanks and sinkholes as a sewer system.

Since sinkholes can serve as points of water concentration [20], the more numerous and closer together they are, the greater the risk of landslides they pose to the nearest dwellings. Finally, the presence of significant signs of instability, as illustrated in Figure 17a,b, including vertical, horizontal and diagonal cracks in floors and/or masonry, and the inclination of rigid structures, such as retaining walls, large trees, fences, posts and sinking floors, were determining factors for the high-risk classification in some sectors of Jacó.

**Figure 16.** (**a**) Presence of water on the slope surface; (**b**) Damaged drain pipe.

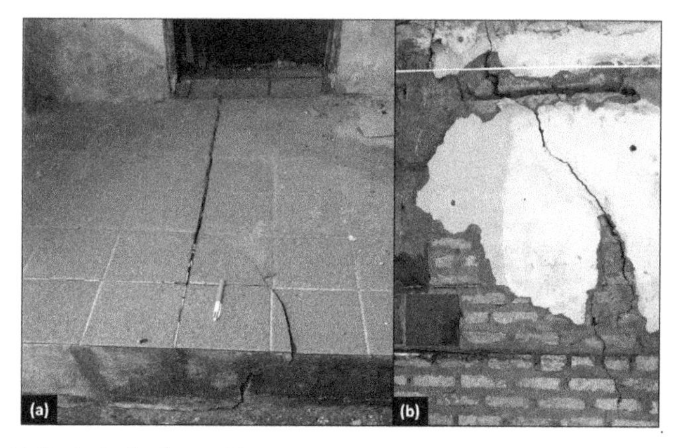

**Figure 17.** (**a**) Cracks in the floors; (**b**) Vertical, horizontal, and diagonal cracks in the masonry of residences in the study area.4. Discussion and Conclusions.

This study aimed to assess and map the risk of landslides in an inhabited urban slope in the municipality of Natal, Rio Grande do Norte state, Brazil, applying an adapted version of Faria's (2011) qualitative-quantitative risk analysis methodology. This methodological proposal incorporated the AHP decision-making tool into a qualitative method of risk analysis.

Mapping the risk of landslides is an essential tool for the definition of land use and occupation policies in urban areas (e.g., [21]). The methodology applied in this study falls well within the range of available techniques used for susceptibility and hazard mapping of landslides [22]. Based on the classification of mapping techniques into qualitative, semi-quantitative and qualitative—where the qualitative techniques are supported by geomorphic analysis and the analysis of landslide inventory that occurred in the studied region while, on the other hand, semi-quantitative techniques are based on multicriteria decision analysis, and the quantitative techniques include statistical and probabilistic analysis, a deterministic approach, and artificial intelligence—the method used in this study can be classified as semi-quantitative.

Regardless of the method used, the inference of risk of landslides can only be made from knowledge of the types and mechanisms acting in the area. In this sense, Ref. [23], based on a recommendation from the Joint Technical Committee on Landslides and Engineered Slopes (JTC-1), highlighted that in the risk mapping the landslide inventory map is essential. On the other hand, there are situations in which there are no files with a record of landslide occurrences, or these records are not reliable where expert evaluations can be used [22].

In the present work, although an inventory map has not been presented, the typology and instability mechanisms have been interpreted from the Civil Defense database in Natal and from the experience reported in previous works developed in the region [4,24–27]. These aspects were considered in the risk map using the presence of instability features indicator. This approach justified the consultation with specialists to establish the weights attributed to the socioenvironmental indicators which, in turn, suggested an acceptable consistency level in the performed comparisons as well as coherence in the order of importance obtained for the attributes and their subclasses, when comparing the research data with information extracted in field visits.

Favorable results in using the combination of GIS and AHP method in terms of mapping areas of susceptibility, hazard, and/or risk were obtained by [8,28,29]. Ref. [8] emphasize that although this type of methodology is considered subjective, the fact that it allows the incorporation of experts' opinions through the attribution of weights to socioenvironmental indicators and adopts a sensitivity analysis to assess the assigned weights has led to reliable results, from larger work scales at the local level, to small mapping scales at the national level.

The risk map obtained by applying an adapted version of [9] demonstrated that the study area exhibits a high degree of slope instability risk in approximately half of the São José do Jacó settlement. This region showed the existence of a number of factors that increase the possibility of landslides, including anthropic interventions in the area, the presence of significant instability features, and a considerable number of residential plots occupied by substandard housing, in addition to a high population density.

This analysis demonstrated that the geomorphological, geological, and geotechnical constraints were less relevant for spatializing risk in the community of São José do Jacó, and that the most important contribution for the occurrence of landslides in the area is the anthropic interference on the slope and the influence of demographic density, a socioenvironmental indicator representative of the elements at risk.

Bearing in mind that the wider study area is relatively densely populated, and in order to prevent loss of life and material damage, civil engineers, land planners, and environmental managers can use the results of this study to pinpoint the risk areas as well as monitor the most critical indicators in the long term. This monitoring program, coupled with an adequate maintenance program for the existing infrastructure and control of any new built infrastructure, can contribute towards the sustainability of the infrastructure, environment, and of the community inhabiting it.

The comparison between the four studies conducted in the São José do Jacó settlement indicated a critical risk situation for the local population, primarily in the form of landslides, causing possible economic, environmental and above all, social harm. The three other studies that investigated the area [30–32] showed similar results, underscoring the area between Desembargador Lins Bahia and CGU Streets as high-risk for the occurrence of landslides.

The observation of consistent similarities between the results of this work and the other mappings already carried out in the study area, as well as the comparison of the mapping result with the data and information obtained from the field visits, were important to validate the acceptability and accuracy of the results achieved by applying the qualitative and quantitative model of [9], which means that a similar approach can be used in the other occupied urban slopes in the city of Natal, or in regions with physical and social characteristics similar to those observed in the study area.

Ref. [21] reviewed 768 scientific articles produced between 1999 and 2018, whose main theme involved the mapping of susceptibility, hazard or risk of landslides, in order to observe, in addition to other aspects, trends in the type of model used in these analyses. Among the several commonly used model types, the AHP method has shown a growth trend in its use over the past 20 years.

Despite the clarity and validation of the results of this study, as well as the flexibility of the model, Ref. [33] points out an important limitation of the method, linked to the inability to determine the uncertainties related to the selection, comparison, and ranking of the multiple criteria analyzed by the experts. Thus, in an attempt to mitigate this limitation, future work should focus on combining the AHP method with another technique, creating integrated models that preserve and integrate the advantages of the models that have been combined.

**Author Contributions:** Conceptualization, L.B., O.d.F.N. and O.S.J.; Methodology, L.B., O.d.F.N., O.S.J. and S.M.; Investigation, L.B., O.d.F.N. and O.S.J.; Writing—original draft, L.B., O.d.F.N., O.S.J. and S.M.; Writing—review & editing, L.B., O.d.F.N., O.S.J. and S.M.; Funding acquisition, L.B., O.d.F.N., O.S.J., S.M.; Resources, L.B., O.d.F.N. and O.S.J., S.M.; Supervision, L.B., O.d.F.N., O.S.J. and S.M. All authors have read and agreed to the published version of the manuscript.

**Funding:** This research was funded by Higher Education Personnel Improvement Coordination—Brazil (CAPES).

**Acknowledgments:** The authors are grateful to the support provided by the Brazilian research sponsorship organizations CNPq (National Council for Scientific and Technological Development), CAPES (Higher Education Personnel Improvement Coordination) and the Municipal Civil Defense team of Natal, Brazil. The authors are also indebted to the Graduate Program Civil Engineering of the Federal University of Rio Grande do Norte (PEC-UFRN).

**Conflicts of Interest:** The authors declare no conflict of interest.

## References

1. International Federation of Red Cross and Red Crescent Societies. World Disasters Report Focus on Urban Risk. 2010. Available online: https://www.ifrc.org/en/publications-and-reports/world-disasters-report/wdr2010// (accessed on 17 September 2020).
2. Universidade Federal de Santa Catarina; Centro Universitário de Estudos e Pesquisas sobre Desastres. *Atlas Brasileiro de Desastres Naturais: 1991 a 2012*, 2nd ed.; CEPED UFSC: Florianópolis, Brazil, 2013.
3. Tominaga, L.K.; Santoro, J.; Amaral, R. *Desastres Naturais: Conhecer Para Prevenir*, 1st ed.; Instituto Geológico: São Paulo, Brazil, 2009.
4. Santos Junior, O.F.; Severo, R.N.F.; Freitas Neto, O. Movimentos de massas em encostas na cidade de Natal/RN. In *Willy Lacerda: Doutor no Saber e Na Arte De Viver*, 1st ed.; Outras Letras: Rio de Janeiro, Brazil, 2016; Volume 1, pp. 468–478.
5. Australian Geomechanics Society; Sub-Committee on Landslide Risk Management. Landslide Risk Management Concepts and Guidelines. *Aust. Geomech. J. News Aust. Geomech. Soci.* **2002**, *37*, 1–44.
6. Van Westen, C.J.; Van Asch, T.W.J.; Soeters, R. Landslide hazard and risk zonation—Why is it still so difficult? *Bull. Eng. Geol. Environ.* **2005**, *65*, 167–184. [CrossRef]
7. Fell, R.; Ho, K.K.S.; Lacasse, S.; Leroi, E. State of the Art: A framework for landslide risk assessment and management. In *Landslide Risk Management*; Hungr, O., Feel, R., Couture, R., Eberhardt, E., Eds.; Taylor and Francis Group: London, UK, 2005; pp. 3–26.
8. Abella, E.A.C.; Van Westen, C.J. Generation of a landslide risk index map for Cuba using spatial multi-criteria evaluation. *Landslides* **2007**, *4*, 311–325. [CrossRef]
9. Faria, D.G.M. Mapeamento de Perigo de Escorregamentos em Áreas Urbanas Precárias Brasileiras Com a Incorporação do Processo de Análise Hierárquica (AHP). Ph.D. Thesis, University of São Paulo, São Paulo, Brazil, 2011.
10. Faria, D.G.M.; Augusto Filho, O. Aplicação do Processo de Análise Hierárquica (AHP) no Mapeamento de Perigo de Escorregamentos em Áreas Urbanas. *Rev. Inst. Geol.* **2013**, *34*, 23–44. [CrossRef]
11. Franek, J.; Kresta, A. Judgment Scales and Consistency Measure in AHP. *Procedia Econ. Financ.* **2014**, *12*, 164–173. [CrossRef]
12. Ministério das Cidades. *Instituto de Pesquisas Tecnológicas—IPT. Mapeamento de Riscos em Encostas e Margem de Rios*; Ministério das Cidades: Brasilia, Brazil; Instituto de Pesquisas Tecnológicas—IPT: Brasília, Brazil, 2007.
13. Saaty, T.L. How to Make a Decision: The Analytic Hierarchy Process. *Eur. J. Oper. Res.* **1990**, *48*, 9–26. [CrossRef]
14. Saaty, T.L. Decision making with the analytic hierarchy process. *Int. J. Serv. Sci.* **2008**, *1*, 83–98. [CrossRef]
15. Saaty, R.W. The analytic hierarchy process—What it is and how it is used. *Math. Model.* **1987**, *9*, 161–176. [CrossRef]

16. Sobrinha, M.D.P.B.; Duarte, M.C.S.; Lélis, R.L.S.; Wanderley, M.U. Vivências, troca de saberes e formação cidadã para o direito à cidade: Experiências do Projeto Motyrum—UFRN, de educação popular em direitos humanos, na Comunidade do Jacó, em Natal/RN. In Proceedings of the Anais XVIII ENANPUR 2019, Encontro Nacional da Associação Nacional de Pós-Graduação e Pesquisa em Planjemanento Urbano e Regional, Natal, Brazil, 27–31 May 2019.
17. Saaty, T.L. A scaling method for priorities in hierarchical structures. *J. Math. Psychol.* **1977**, *15*, 234–281. [CrossRef]
18. Instituto Brasileiro de Geografia e Estatística—IBGE. *Características da População e dos Domicílios: Resultados do Universo*; IBGE: Rio de Janeiro, Brazil, 2011.
19. Wiggers, M.M. Zoneamento das Áreas de Risco a Movimentos de Massa no Perímetro Urbano do Município de Caxias do Sul (RS). Master's Thesis, Federal University of Rio Grande do Sul, Porto Alegre, Brazil, 2013.
20. Alheiros, M.M.; Souza, M.A.A.; Bitoun, J.; Medeiros, S.M.G.M.; Amorim Júnior, W.M. *Manual de Ocupação dos Morros da Região Metropolitana do Recife*; FIDEM: Recife, Brazil, 2003.
21. Lee, S. Current and Future Status of GIS-based Landslide Susceptibility Mapping: A Literature Review. *Korean J. Remote Sens.* **2019**, *35*, 179–193. [CrossRef]
22. Shano, L.; Raghuvanshi, T.K.; Meten, M. Landslide susceptibility evaluation and hazard zonation techniques—A review. *Geoenviron. Disasters* **2020**, *7*, 1–19. [CrossRef]
23. Cascini, L. Applicability of landslide susceptibility and hazard zoning at different scales. *Eng. Geol.* **2008**, *102*, 164–177. [CrossRef]
24. Santos, O.F., Jr.; Jesus, A.P.; Macêdo, C.M.H.; Amaral, R.F. Mapeamento de Áreas de Risco de Movimentos de Massas em Encostas Formadas por Dunas na Cidade de Natal. In Proceedings of the Anais XI Congresso Brasileiro de Mecânica dos Solos e Engenharia Geotécnica, Brasília, Brazil, 6–10 November 1998; pp. 521–527.
25. Barbosa, N.; Taquez, D.; Santos, O., Jr.; Freitas Neto, O.; Scudelari, A. The Effect of Basal Erosion on Sea Cliff Stability. *J. Coast. Res.* **2020**, *95*, 362–366. [CrossRef]
26. Silva, B.M.F.; Santos , O.F., Jr.; Neto, O.F.; Scudelari, A.C. Erosão em Falésias Costeiras e Movimentos de Massa no Rio Grande do Norte, Nordeste do Brasil. *Geociências* **2020**, *39*, 447–461. [CrossRef]
27. Souza, P.L., Jr.; Santos, O.F., Jr.; Fontoura, T.B.; Freitas Neto, O. Drained and Undrained Behavior of an Aeolian Sand from Natal, Brazil. *Soils Rocks* **2020**, *43*, 263–270. [CrossRef]
28. Lorentz, J.F.; Calijuri, M.L.; Marques, E.G.; Baptista, A.C. Multicriteria analysis applied to landslide susceptibility mapping. *Nat. Hazard* **2016**, *83*, 41–52. [CrossRef]
29. El Jazouli, A.; Barakat, A.; Khellouk, R. GIS-multicriteria evaluation using AHP for landslide susceptibility mapping in Oum Er Rbia high basin (Morocco). *Geoenviron. Disasters* **2019**, *6*, 3. [CrossRef]
30. Prefeitura do Natal; Secretaria Municipal de Meio Ambiente e Urbanismo—SEMURB. *Plano Municipal de Gerenciamento de Riscos: Relatório Final—Volume 1*; Acquatool Consultoria: Natal, Brazil, 2008.
31. Silva, E.E.S.; Almeida, L.Q.; Macedo, Y.M. Uso de metodologia analítica para mapeamento de exposição ao risco de deslizamento na comunidade de São José do Jacó Natal—RN. *Rev. Geociênc. Nordeste* **2016**, *1*, 58–73.
32. Bezerra, L.T.V. Mapeamento de Risco/perigo de Movimentos de Massa e Avaliação da Estabilidade das Encostas na Comunidade São José do Jacó, em Natal/RN. Bachelor's Thesis, Federal University of Rio Grande do Norte, Natal, Brazil, 2016.
33. Zhou, S.; Chen, G.; Fang, L.; Nie, Y. GIS-Based Integration of Subjective and Objective Weighting Methods for Regional Landslides Susceptibility Mapping. *Sustainability* **2016**, *8*, 334. [CrossRef]


**Publisher's Note:** MDPI stays neutral with regard to jurisdictional claims in published maps and institutional affiliations.

*Article*

# Strength Performance and Microstructure of Calcium Sulfoaluminate Cement-Stabilized Soft Soil

**Hailong Liu [1,2], Jiuye Zhao [1], Yu Wang [1], Nangai Yi [1,*] and Chunyi Cui [1]**

[1] Department of Civil Engineering, Dalian Maritime University, Dalian 116026, China; liuhailong@dlmu.edu.cn (H.L.); zhaojiuye@dlmu.edu.cn (J.Z.); wangyu2018@dlmu.edu.cn (Y.W.); cuichunyi@dlmu.edu.cn (C.C.)

[2] MOE Key Laboratory of Soft Soils and Geoenvironmental Engineering, Zhejiang University, Hangzhou 310058, China

* Correspondence: yinangai@dlmu.edu.cn

**Abstract:** Calcium sulfoaluminate cement (CSA) was used to stabilize a type of marine soft soil in Dalian China. Unconfined compressive strength (UCS) of CSA-stabilized soil was tested and compared to ordinary Portland cement (OPC); meanwhile the influence of amounts of gypsum in CSA and cement contents in stabilized soils on the strength of stabilized soils were investigated. X-ray diffraction (XRD) tests were employed to detect generated hydration products, and scanning electron microscopy (SEM) was conducted to analyze microstructures of CSA-stabilized soils. The results showed that UCS of CSA-stabilized soils at 1, 3, and 28 d firstly increased and then decreased with contents of gypsum increasing from 0 to 40 wt.%, and CSA-stabilized soils exhibited the highest UCS when the content of gypsum equaled 25 wt.%. When the mixing amounts of OPC and CSA were the same, CSA-stabilized soils had a significantly higher early strength (1 and 3 d) than OPC. For CSA-stabilized soil with 0 wt.% gypsum, monosulfate (AFm) was detected as a major hydration product. As for CSA-stabilized soil with certain amounts of gypsum, the intensity of ettringite (Aft) was significantly higher than that in the sample hydrating without gypsum, but a tiny peak of AFm also could be detected in the sample with 15 wt.% gypsum at 28 d. Additionally, the intensity of AFt increased with the contents of gypsum increasing from 0 to 25 wt.%. When contents of gypsum increased from 25 to 40 wt.%, the intensity of AFt tended to decrease slightly, and residual gypsum could be detected in the sample with 40 wt.% gypsum at 28 d. In the microstructure of OPC-stabilized soils, hexagonal plate-shaped calcium hydroxide (CH) constituted skeleton structures, and clusters of hydrated calcium silicates (C-S-H) gel adhered to particles of soils. In the microstructure of CSA-stabilized soils, AFt constituted skeleton structures, and the crystalline sizes of ettringite increased with contents of gypsum increasing; meanwhile, clusters of the aluminum hydroxide ($AH_3$) phase could be observed to adhere to particles of soils and strengthen the interaction.

**Keywords:** calcium sulfoaluminate cement; stabilized soil; unconfined compressive strength; hydration products; microstructure; sustainability

**Citation:** Liu, H.; Zhao, J.; Wang, Y.; Yi, N.; Cui, C. Strength Performance and Microstructure of Calcium Sulfoaluminate Cement-Stabilized Soft Soil. *Sustainability* **2021**, *13*, 2295. https://doi.org/10.3390/su13042295

Academic Editor: Slobodan B. Mickovski

Received: 31 January 2021
Accepted: 17 February 2021
Published: 20 February 2021



## 1. Introduction

Soft soil deposits exist all over the planet, such as in the economically developed areas located on the southeast coast of China. Land resources are becoming increasingly scarce with the development and expansion of these cities. As a result, a large number of structures need to be built on soft soil foundations. Soft soil is often a challenge for engineers due to the mechanical properties of poor bearing capacity, low shear strength, and high compressibility [1–5]. To improve the engineering performance of soft soils, a series of methods including cement-based stabilization, alkali-activated treatment, and carbonation techniques are conducted in geotechnical engineering [6–11]. Studies have indicated that cementation can alter the characteristics of soil behaviors and significantly improve the strength properties of soft soil. For example, artificial cementation has been applied for soil stabilization, for column-type reinforcement in soft soils, in gravity composite structures, for liquefaction mitigation, and as in-place barriers for cutting off seepage [12–14]. Cement-based stabilization is the most common method for enhancing the performance of soft soils used in construction projects, in which ordinary Portland cement (OPC) is always chosen as the binder owing to its easy availability, and extensive literature is available for reference [15–19]. OPC-treated soil has improved bearing capacity and reduced permeability and compressibility [20,21]. For OPC-stabilized soft soils, the strength mainly originates from hydration reactions of minerals in OPC; furthermore, hydrated calcium silicates (abbreviated as C-S-H, in this paper cement abbreviation has been used as followed C: CaO, S: $SiO_2$, A: $Al_2O_3$, $: $SO_3$, H: $H_2O$) and calcium hydroxide ($Ca(OH)_2$, abbreviated as CH) are the main hydration products [1,22]. Besides, it should be noted that potential pozzolanic reactions between calcium hydroxide and alkali active admixtures also contribute to the strength of OPC-based stabilization in the long term [23].

However, OPC also exhibited a limitation of engineering performance in several aspects, such as relatively low strength development, and inclined erosion of hardened pastes [24,25]. On the other hand, OPC poses significant environmental concerns associated with carbon dioxide ($CO_2$) emissions released during its manufacturing process. With the annually increased consumption of OPC, there is a strong need for sustainable development [26–28]. To improve the performance of cement-based materials and reduce $CO_2$ emissions, special types of cement were applied as an alternative to OPC in certain situations, in which calcium sulfoaluminate (CSA) cement has attracted attention [29–32]. CSA has characters of rapid hardening, high early strength, resistance to sulfate attack, and tailored expansion [33]. The main components of CSA are ye'elimite ($C_4A_3\$$), belite ($C_2S$) and gypsum ($C\${\cdot}H_2$), and the main hydration of CSA at an early stage is the reaction between $C_4A_3\$$ and $C\${\cdot}H_2$ [30,34,35].

In previous studies related to CSA cement-based stabilization, Gastaldi et al. [36] studied the hydration of CSA cement with different contents of sulfate and silicate. Vinoth et al. [37] investigated the early strength development of two types of CSA cement using ultrasonic pulse velocity and measuring unconfined compressive strength. Li and Chang [38] examined the effects of $C\${\cdot}H_2$ on the CSA hydration system investigating the mechanical properties, hydration process, and hydration mechanism. Lan and Glasser [39] investigated CSA cement hydration by studying scanning electron microscope images and isothermal calorimetry of CSA cements, simulating various clinker mineralogies including lime, $C\${\cdot}H_2$, $C_2S$, and CSA. Tang et al. [40] investigated the hydration stages and phase transformation between ettringite and monosulfate of CSA cement. Winnefeld and Lothenbach [27] studied the hydration of CSA with different water-to-cement ratios.

However, the use of CSA cement in geotechnical applications has been explored in a limited way as yet. Furthermore, soil structure is different from that of cement paste; hence the experience gained from cement paste cannot be applied directly in soft soil stabilization [13,28,41]. In this paper, CSA was used to stabilize a type of marine soft soil in Dalian China. The strength of CSA-stabilized soil was tested and compared to that of OPC; meanwhile, the influence of amounts of $C\${\cdot}H_2$ in CSA and cement content in stabilized soils on the strength of stabilized soils were investigated. X-ray diffraction (XRD) tests were employed to detect generated hydration products; meanwhile, a scanning electron microscope (SEM) was used to analyze microstructures of CSA-stabilized soils.

## 2. Materials and Methods

### 2.1. Raw Materials of the Experiments

In this manuscript, soft soil was collected from a coastal region in Dalian, a city in northeast China. OPC and CSA clinker were commercial products and purchased from Xiaoyetian Cement Company and Beijixiong Cement Company, respectively. $C\${\cdot}H_2$ was an analytic reagent. Chemical compositions and particle size distributions of raw materials are respectively shown in Table 1 and Figure 1.

**Table 1.** Chemical composition of raw materials (wt.%).

| Raw Materials | CaO | $Fe_2O_3$ | MgO | $Al_2O_3$ | $SiO_2$ | $SO_3$ | $Na_2O$ | $K_2O$ | $TiO_2$ | Others |
|---|---|---|---|---|---|---|---|---|---|---|
| Soft soil | 5.55 | 8.65 | 6.41 | 22.48 | 43.88 | 0.83 | 3.42 | 5.77 | 2.19 | 0.82 |
| OPC | 73.74 | 3.42 | 3.50 | 5.82 | 9.15 | 1.86 | 0.29 | 0.90 | 0.88 | 0.44 |
| CSA clinker | 53.95 | 2.23 | 2.60 | 29.04 | 3.28 | 4.85 | 0.13 | 0.75 | 2.93 | 0.24 |
| Gypsum | 41.18 | - | - | - | - | 58.82 | - | - | - | - |

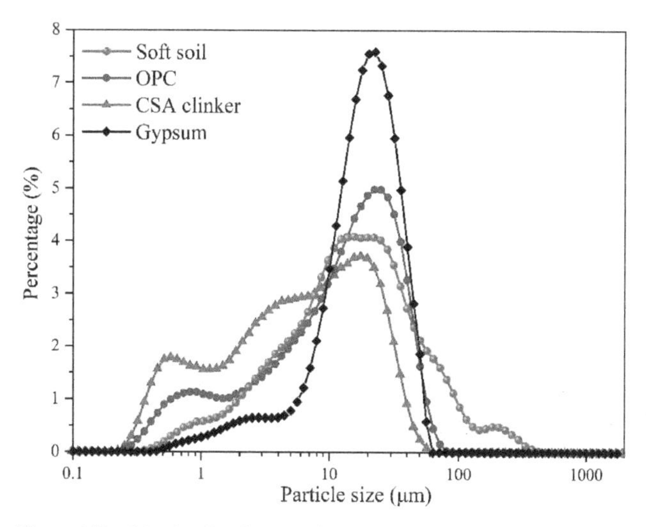


**Figure 1.** Particle size distribution of raw materials.

## 2.2. Specimen Preparation

Collected soft soils were firstly dried in an oven at 100 °C for 24 h and sieved through passing a sieve with 2 mm mesh. Afterward, dried and sieved soils were mixed with distilled water to prepare wet soils with a water content of 41%, which was closed to the natural moisture content of the soft soils. CSA clinker and different amounts of $C\$ {\cdot} H_2$ were mixed to prepare CSA, and $C\$ {\cdot} H_2$ respectively accounted for 0, 5, 10, 15, 20, 25, 30, 35, and 40 wt.% in CSA. For both OPC and CSA, grouts with a binder ratio of 0.5 were prepared, and then adequately mixed with the wet soils. The procedure above simulated treating processes in practical engineering to the maximum extent. After mixing, pastes were poured into a cylindrical mold measuring $\varphi 5 \times H10$ cm and cured with sealed plastic wraps in a chamber under conditions of 20 ± 2 °C and more than 95% relative humidity.

## 2.3. Methods of Tests

After curing for 1, 3, and 28 d, specimens of stabilized soils were tested for unconfined compressive strength (UCS) according to ASTMD-2166 (American Society of Testing Materials). The rate of loading was controlled to be 1.00 mm/min. For each UCS test, six specimens were tested to obtain the average value and standard deviation.

At curing ages of 1, 3, and 28 d, a certain amount of crashed hardened paste of stabilized soil was immersed in isopropanol to remove free water and terminate hydration. After immersing for 24 h, the hardened pastes of stabilized soils were dried at 35 °C and ground to pass a sieve with 45 μm mesh. XRD was conducted on a Bruker D8 advance Davinci design X-ray diffractometer ($CuK\alpha_{1,2}$ radiation, $\lambda_1 = 0.15406$ nm, $\lambda_2 = 0.15444$ nm) to test the ground pastes of stabilized soils. The operating voltage and current were 40 kV and 40 mA, respectively. Patterns of XRD were collected from 5 to 120° (2θ) with a 0.02° step size, and each step time equaled 0.1 s. To determine the phases in pastes of stabilized soils, Evolution (Bruker) software was used to analyze obtained patterns with the crystallographic database of ICDD-PDF 2019.

To characterize the microstructures of stabilized soils, the scanning electron microscopy (SEM) test was performed on a field emission scanning electron microscope (Zeiss ΣIGMA HD type) with an accelerating voltage of 3/5 kV to examine crushed pieces of hardened paste.

## 3. Results and Discussion

### 3.1. UCS of CSA-Stabilized Soil

Gypsum is a significant part of CSA cement, and there is an optimal content of C\$·$H_2$ in CSA cement for mortar or concrete of CSA cement. To investigate the influence of contents of C\$·$H_2$ on CSA-stabilized soils, the UCS of CSA-stabilized soils with different C\$·$H_2$ contents were compared in Figure 2 (for both CSA and OPC-stabilized soils in Figure 2, the ratio of cement to dry soils equaled 0.12).

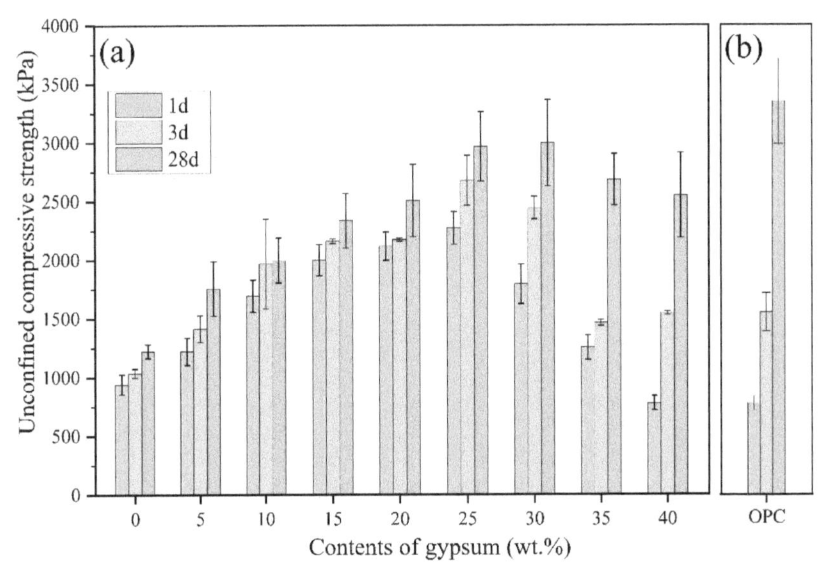


**Figure 2.** Influence of contents of gypsum on calcium sulfoaluminate cement (CSA)-stabilized soils: (**a**) unconfined compressive strength (UCS) of CSA-stabilized soils with different gypsum contents, (**b**) UCS of ordinary Portland cement (OPC)-stabilized soils.

As Figure 2 shows, for CSA-stabilized soils, UCS of CSA-stabilized soils at 1, 3, and 28 d firstly increased and then decreased with contents of C\$·$H_2$ increasing from 0 to 40 wt.%, and CSA-stabilized soils exhibited the highest UCS when contents of C\$·$H_2$ equaled 25 wt.%. It should also be noted that when contents of C\$·$H_2$ varied from 0 to 25 wt.%, early strength (1 and 3 d) of CSA-stabilized soils generally exceeded 60% of the strength at 28 d. However, when contents of C\$·$H_2$ were more than 25 wt.%, early strength of CSA-stabilized soils significantly decreased. In terms of early strength, the UCS of CSA-stabilized soils with optimal content of C\$·$H_2$ (25 wt.%) was more than twice that of OPC-stabilized soils. However, for strength at 28 d, the UCS of OPC-stabilized soils was higher than that of all CSA-stabilized soils. Even UCS of CSA-stabilized soils with optimal content of C\$·$H_2$ (the optimal content of C\$·$H_2$ for the CSA-stabilized soils was 25 wt.%, with the maximum UCS being 2966 kPa) was slightly less than that of OPC-stabilized soils (USC = 3348 kPa). To further investigate the influence of mixing amounts of cement on stabilized soils, the UCS of OPC and CSA-stabilized soils are compared in Figure 3.

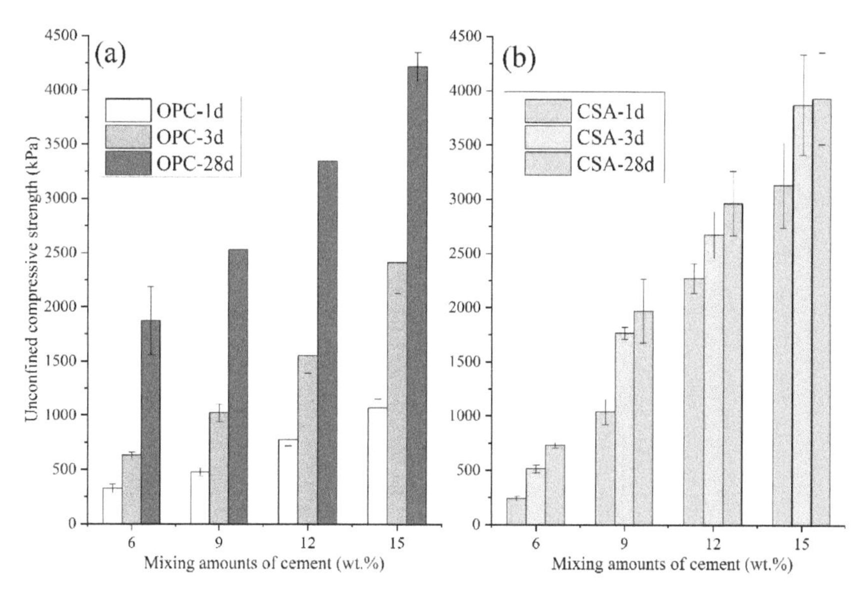


**Figure 3.** Influence of mixing amounts for different types of cement on UCS of stabilized soils.

As shown in Figure 3, for both CSA and OPC-stabilized soils, UCS at 1, 3, and 28 d gradually increased with mixing amounts of cement increasing from 6 to 15 wt.%. Meanwhile, it can be also observed that, for stabilized soils with any mixing amounts of OPC, early strength at 1 and 3 d only achieved approximately 30% and 50% strength at 28 d, respectively. On the other hand, for stabilized soils with any mixing amounts of CSA, early strength at 1 and 3 d was more than the 50% and 80% strength at 28 d, respectively. It should be also noted that, when the mixing amounts of OPC and CSA were the same, strength of OPC-stabilized soils at 28 d was greater than that of CSA, which was more obvious for mixing amounts of 6 and 9 wt.%. The strength development of stabilized soils mainly resulted from continuous hydration of CSA and OPC which prolonged until 28 d; in particular, $C_2S$ in both CSA and OPC contributed more to long-term strength.

### *3.2. Hydration Products of CSA-Stabilized Soil*

To investigate the hydration products in OPC and CSA-stabilized soils, XRD tests were conducted. For determining the distribution ranges of peaks for hydration products, XRD patterns of OPC and CSA-stabilized soils with 0 and 40 wt.% $C\$\cdot H_2$ at 28 d were chosen to exhibit in Figure 4 (for all patterns, mixing amounts for different types of cement equaled 12 wt.%).

As Figure 4 shows, certain peaks of all three patterns were overlapped and attributed to minerals in the soft soil, such as quartz (major peak at 26.7°), muscovite (major peak at 8.9°), and potash feldspar (major peak at 27.6°). It should be noted that major minerals in the soft soils, including quartz, muscovite, and potash feldspar, are primary minerals with relatively inert activation, which tend to be stable in cement slurries [42,43]. Additionally, the peaks for minerals in the soft soil remained stable during the hydration process of CSA and OPC; thus this paper has not considered chemical interaction between the minerals in the soft soil used in this paper and cement or the hydration products. Meanwhile, certain peaks in the XRD patterns can be attributed to hydration products of OPC or CSA. For OPC-stabilized soil, CH can be detected as a major crystalline hydration product on account of a peak at 18.1°. The formation of CH mainly resulted from the hydration of $C_3S$ and partial $C_2S$. According to the stoichiometry of typical C-S-H found in hydrated OPC, hydration of $C_3S$ and $C_2S$ can be described by Equation (1) and Equation (2) [44]. As for CSA-stabilized soil, AFt and AFm can be detected as major crystalline hydration products due to hydration of $C_4A_3\$$; meanwhile, residual $C\$\cdot H_2$ can also be observed. It can be also noted that the major peaks for AFt, AFm, and $C\$\cdot H_2$ were concentrated in the range of 6–14°. To further investigate the influence of amounts of $C\$\cdot H_2$ and hydration age on hydration products in CSA-stabilized soils, XRD patterns in the range of 6–14° of CSA-stabilized soils with different amounts of $C\$\cdot H_2$ at different hydration ages were compared in Figure 5.

$$C_3S + 5.3H \rightarrow 1.3CH + C_{1.7}SH_4 \quad (1)$$

$$C_2S + 4.3H \rightarrow 0.3CH + C_{1.7}SH_4 \quad (2)$$

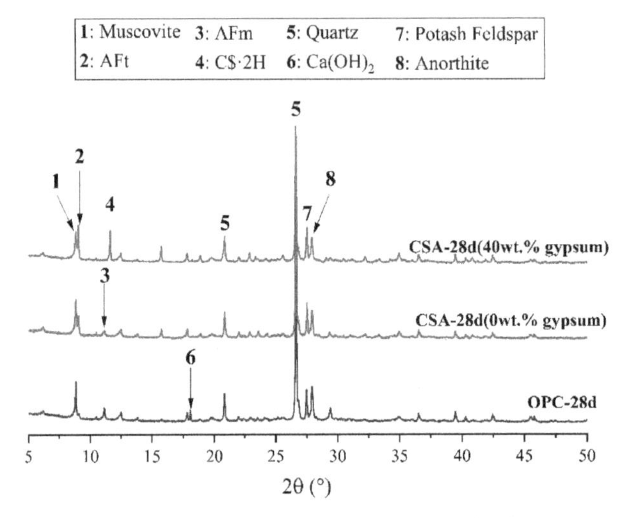


**Figure 4.** Typical XRD patterns of OPC- and CSA-stabilized soils.

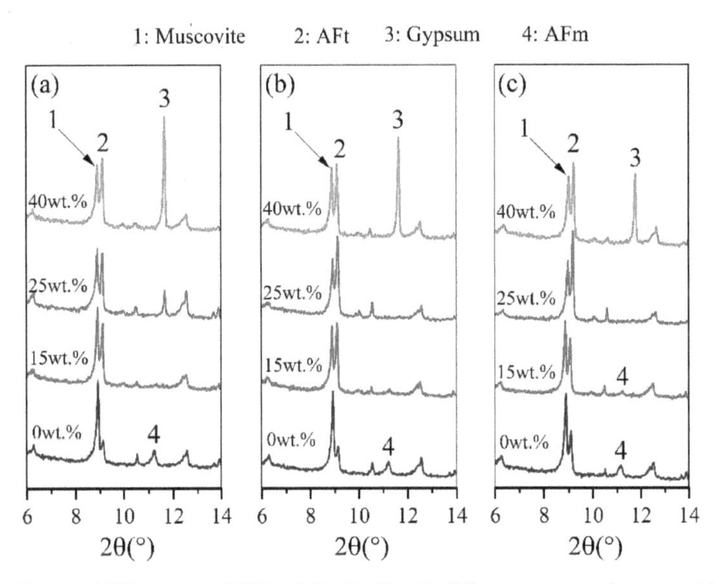


**Figure 5.** XRD patterns of CSA-stabilized soils with different amounts of gypsum: (**a**) hydration age of 1 d, (**b**) hydration age of 3 d, (**c**) hydration age of 28 d.

According to the results in Figure 5, it can be seen that for CSA-stabilized soil with 0 wt.% $C\$ \cdot H_2$, AFm can be observed, and the formation of AFm can be attributed to hydration of $C_4A_3\$$ without $C\$ \cdot H_2$, which can be described by Equation (3). Meanwhile, a relatively low-intensity peak for AFt can be also detected at 9.2° in the sample without $C\$ \cdot H_2$. The formation of small quantities of AFt was attributed to the supersaturation of sulfate ions at a very early stage of hydration; additionally, sulfate ions in soft soils can also contribute to the formation of AFt. As for CSA-stabilized soil with certain amounts of $C\$ \cdot H_2$, it can be observed that the intensity of AFt was significantly higher than that in the samples without $C\$ \cdot H_2$; meanwhile, a tiny peak of AFm can be detected in the sample with 15 wt.% $C\$ \cdot H_2$ at 28 d. Additionally, it also can be noted that the intensity of AFt increased with the contents of $C\$ \cdot H_2$ increasing from 0 to 25 wt.%. However, when contents of $C\$ \cdot H_2$ increased from 25 to 40 wt.%, the intensity of AFt tended to decrease slightly, and residual $C\$ \cdot H_2$ can be detected in the sample with 40 wt.% $C\$ \cdot H_2$ at 28 d. Based on the results of previous studies, in the condition of hydrating with $C\$ \cdot H_2$, $C_4A_3\$$ prioritizes to hydrate with $C\$ \cdot H_2$, and the reaction can be described by Equation (4). After gypsum is thoroughly consumed, $C_4A_3\$$ continues to react according to Equation (3), which leads to the formation of AFm. Trends of intensity for AFt and $C\$ \cdot H_2$ in samples of hydrating with $C\$ \cdot H_2$ illustrates that for the sample with 15 wt.% gypsum, both reactions of Equation (3) and Equation (4) occurred during 28 d hydrating age. As for the sample with 25 wt.% $C\$ \cdot H_2$, $C\$ \cdot H_2$ was adequate for the reaction of Equation (4). When the content of $C\$ \cdot H_2$ equaled 40 wt.%, certain amounts of $C\$ \cdot H_2$ were residual after the reaction of Equation (4).

$$C_4A_3\$ + 18H \rightarrow C_4A\$H_{12} + 2AH_3 \quad (3)$$

$$C_4A_3\$ + 2(C\$ \cdot H_2) + 34H \rightarrow C_6A\$_3H_{32} + 2AH_3 \quad (4)$$

### 3.3. *Distinction of Microstructures between OPC- and CSA-Stabilized Soils*

Figure 6 shows the SEM images of OPC- and CSA-stabilized soils. As shown in Figure 6a, hexagonal plate-shaped CH and gelatinous C-S-H can be observed in the microstructure for OPC-stabilized soils. Hexagonal plate-shaped CH constituted skeleton structures, and the size approximately ranged from 1 to 3 μm. Meanwhile, clusters of C-S-H gel adhered to particles of soils, which strengthened the interaction among soil particles.

As for microstructures of CSA-stabilized soils (see Figure 6b–d), AFt with characters of needle bar granular and nemaline $AH_3$ can be observed. Differing from the microstructure of OPC-stabilized soils, the needle bar-shaped AFt constituted skeleton structures, and the sizes of ettringite impacted by contents of $C\$ \cdot H_2$. Specifically, the sizes of ettringite fluctuated around 1 μm when the content of $C\$ \cdot H_2$ equaled 10 wt.% (see Figure 6b). With a content of $C\$ \cdot H_2$ increasing to 20 wt.%, sizes of ettringite increased to range from around 2 to 3 μm (see Figure 6c). As shown in Figure 6d, the largest size of ettringite increased to be more than 4 μm when the content of $C\$ \cdot H_2$ equaled 25 wt.%. Additionally, for CSA-stabilized soils with different $C\$ \cdot H_2$ contents, clusters of $AH_3$ phase could be observed to adhere to particles of soils and strengthen the interaction, which was similar to that of C-S-H gel in OPC-stabilized soils.

**Figure 6.** SEM images of OPC- and CSA-stabilized soils: (**a**) OPC-stabilized soils, (**b**) CSA-stabilized soils with 10 wt.% gypsum, (**c**) CSA-stabilized soils with 20 wt.% gypsum, (**d**) CSA-stabilized soils with 25 wt.% gypsum.

## 4. Conclusions

Strength performance and microstructure of CSA- and OPC-stabilized soft soils were compared. Based on test results of UCS, XRD, and SEM, the following conclusions can be obtained:

(1) UCS of CSA-stabilized soils at 1, 3, and 28 d firstly increased and then decreased with contents of $C\$ \cdot H_2$ increasing from 0 to 40 wt.%. The optimum $C\$ \cdot H_2$ content for CSA-stabilized soils was 25 wt.%, which means the stabilized soils had the highest UCS. When the mixing amounts of OPC and CSA were the same, CSA-stabilized soils had significantly higher early strength (1 and 3 d) than OPC and similar strength at 28 d.

(2) For CSA-stabilized soil with 0 wt.% $C\$ \cdot H_2$, AFm was detected as a major hydration product. As for CSA-stabilized soil with certain amounts of $C\$ \cdot H_2$, the intensity of AFt was significantly higher than that in the sample hydrating without $C\$ \cdot H_2$; meanwhile, a tiny peak of AFm could be also detected in the sample with 15 wt.% $C\$ \cdot H_2$ at 28 d. Additionally, the intensity of AFt increased with the contents of gypsum increasing from 0 to 25 wt.%. When contents of $C\$ \cdot H_2$ increased from 25 to 40 wt.%, the intensity of AFt tended to decrease slightly, and residual $C\$ \cdot H_2$ could be detected in the sample with 40 wt.% $C\$ \cdot H_2$ at 28 d.

(3) In the microstructure of OPC-stabilized soils, hexagonal plate-shaped CH constituted skeleton structures, and clusters of C-S-H gel adhered to particles of soils. In the microstructure of CSA-stabilized soils, AFt constituted skeleton structures, and the crystalline sizes of ettringite increased with contents of $C\$ \cdot H_2$ increasing, meanwhile,

clusters of $AH_3$ phase could be observed to adhere to particles of soils and strengthen the interaction.

**Author Contributions:** Conceptualization, H.L. and C.C.; methodology, H.L.; software, N.Y. and J.Z.; validation, J.Z., Y.W. and C.C.; formal analysis, J.Z.; investigation, N.Y. and Y.W.; resources, N.Y.; data curation, J.Z. and Y.W.; writing—original draft preparation, H.L.; writing—review and editing, J.Z. and C.C.; visualization, N.Y. and H.L.; supervision, H.L.; project administration, H.L. and C.C.; funding acquisition, H.L. All authors have read and agreed to the published version of the manuscript.

**Funding:** This research was funded by the National Natural Science Foundation of China (NSFC), grant number 52008071; the Natural Science Foundation of Liaoning Province, grant number 2019ZD0150; Key Laboratory of Soft Soils and Geoenvironmental Engineering (Zhejiang University), Ministry of Education, grant number 2019P01; Key Laboratory of Ministry of Education for Geomechanics and Embankment Engineering, Hohai University, grant number 201802, and the United Navigation Foundation of Liaoning Province, grant number 2020-HYLH-48.

**Institutional Review Board Statement:** Not applicable.

**Informed Consent Statement:** Not applicable.

**Data Availability Statement:** Data sharing is not applicable to this article.

**Conflicts of Interest:** The authors declare that they have no conflict of interest.

## References

1. Ekinci, A. Effect of preparation methods on strength and microstructural properties of cemented marine clay. *Constr. Build. Mater.* **2019**, *227*, 116690. [CrossRef]
2. Kang, G.; Tsuchida, T.; Kim, Y. Strength and stiffness of cement-treated marine dredged clay at various curing stages. *Constr. Build. Mater.* **2017**, *132*, 71–84. [CrossRef]
3. Kun, M.; Chunyi, C.; Haijiang, L. An Ontology Framework for Pile Integrity Evaluation Based on Analytical Methodology. *IEEE Access* **2020**, *99*, 72158–72168.
4. Yi, Y.; Li, C.; Liu, S.; Al-Tabbaa, A. Resistance of MgO–GGBS and CS–GGBS stabilised marine soft clays to sodium sulfate attack. *Géotechnique* **2014**, *64*, 673–679. [CrossRef]
5. Ho, T.O.; Chen, W.B.; Yin, J.H.; Wu, P.C.; Tsang, D.C. Stress-Strain behaviour of Cement-Stabilized Hong Kong marine deposits. *Constr. Build. Mater.* **2021**, *274*, 122103. [CrossRef]
6. Mickovski, S.B.; Stokes, A.; Van Beek, R.; Ghestem, M.; Fourcaud, T. Simulation of direct shear tests on rooted and non-rooted soil using finite element analysis. *Ecol. Eng.* **2011**, *37*, 1523–1532. [CrossRef]
7. Lang, L.; Liu, N.; Chen, B. Strength development of solidified dredged sludge containing humic acid with cement, lime and nano-$SiO_2$. *Constr. Build. Mater.* **2020**, *230*, 116971. [CrossRef]
8. Jamshidi, R.J.; Lake, C.B. Hydraulic and strength properties of unexposed and freeze–thaw exposed cement-stabilized soils. *Can. Geotech. J.* **2015**, *52*, 283–294. [CrossRef]
9. Yi, Y.; Gu, L.; Liu, S.; Puppala, A.J. Carbide slag–activated ground granulated blastfurnace slag for soft clay stabilization. *Can. Geotech. J.* **2015**, *52*, 656–663. [CrossRef]
10. Robayo, R.A.; Mulford, A.; Munera, J.; de Gutiérrez, R.M. Alternative cements based on alkali-activated red clay brick waste. *Constr. Build. Mater.* **2016**, *128*, 163–169. [CrossRef]
11. Cui, C.; Meng, K.; Xu, C.; Liang, Z.; Li, H.; Pei, H. Analytical solution for longitudinal vibration of a floating pile in saturated porous media based on a fictitious saturated soil pile model. *Comput. Geotech.* **2021**, *131*, 103942. [CrossRef]
12. Yi, Y.; Li, C.; Liu, S. Alkali-Activated Ground-Granulated Blast Furnace Slag for Stabilization of Marine Soft Clay. *J. Mater. Civil Eng.* **2015**, *27*, 04014146. [CrossRef]
13. Subramanian, S.; Moon, S.W.; Moon, J.; Ku, T. CSA-treated sand for geotechnical application: Microstructure analysis and rapid strength development. *J. Mater. Civil Eng.* **2018**, *30*, 04018313. [CrossRef]
14. Kim, G.M.; Jang, J.G.; Khalid, H.R.; Lee, H.K. Water purification characteristics of pervious concrete fabricated with CSA cement and bottom ash aggregates. *Constr. Build. Mater.* **2017**, *136*, 1–8. [CrossRef]
15. Ghadir, P.; Ranjbar, N. Clayey soil stabilization using geopolymer and Portland cement. *Constr. Build. Mater.* **2018**, *188*, 361–371. [CrossRef]
16. Uchima, J.S.; Restrepo-Baena, O.J.; Tobón, J.I. Mineralogical evolution of portland cement blended with metakaolin obtained in simultaneous calcination of kaolinitic clay and rice husk. *Constr. Build. Mater.* **2016**, *118*, 286–293. [CrossRef]
17. Behnood, A. Soil and clay stabilization with calcium- and non-calcium-based additives: A state-of-the-art review of challenges, approaches and techniques. *Transp. Geotech.* **2018**, *17*, 14–32. [CrossRef]

18. Muvuna, J.; Boutaleb, T.; Mickovski, S.B.; Baker, K.; Mohammad, G.S.; Cools, M.; Selmi, W. Information integration in a smart city system—A case study on air pollution removal by green infrastructure through a vehicle smart routing system. *Sustainability* **2020**, *12*, 5099. [CrossRef]
19. Yoon, H.N.; Seo, J.; Kim, S.; Lee, H.K.; Park, S. Hydration of calcium sulfoaluminate cement blended with blast-furnace slag. *Constr. Build. Mater.* **2021**, *268*, 121214. [CrossRef]
20. Horpibulsuk, S.; Rachan, R.; Chinkulkijniwat, A.; Raksachon, Y.; Suddeepong, A. Analysis of strength development in cement-stabilized silty clay from microstructural considerations. *Constr. Build. Mater.* **2010**, *24*, 2011–2021. [CrossRef]
21. Lorenzo, G.A.; Bergado, D.T. Fundamental parameters of cement-admixed clay—New approach. *J. Geotech. Geoenvir. Eng.* **2004**, *130*, 1042–1050. [CrossRef]
22. Wu, J.; Deng, Y.; Zheng, X.; Cui, Y.; Zhao, Z.; Chen, Y.; Zha, F. Hydraulic conductivity and strength of foamed cement-stabilized marine clay. *Constr. Build. Mater.* **2019**, *222*, 688–698. [CrossRef]
23. Liu, L.; Zhou, A.; Deng, Y.; Cui, Y.; Yu, Z.; Yu, C. Strength performance of cement/slag-based stabilized soft clays. *Constr. Build. Mater.* **2019**, *211*, 909–918. [CrossRef]
24. Shi, C.; Jiménez, A.F.; Palomo, A. New cements for the 21st century: The pursuit of an alternative to Portland cement. *Cem. Concr. Res.* **2011**, *41*, 750–763. [CrossRef]
25. Zhou, Q.; Milestone, N.B.; Hayes, M. An alternative to Portland Cement for waste encapsulation—The calcium sulfoaluminate cement system. *J. Hazard. Mater.* **2006**, *136*, 120–129. [CrossRef]
26. Muvuna, J.; Boutaleb, T.; Baker, K.J.; Mickovski, S.B. A methodology to model integrated smart city system from the information perspective. *Smart Cities* **2019**, *2*, 496–511. [CrossRef]
27. Winnefeld, F.; Lothenbach, B. Hydration of calcium sulfoaluminate cements—Experimental findings and thermodynamic modelling. *Cement Concr. Res.* **2010**, *40*, 1239–1247. [CrossRef]
28. Seo, J.; Kim, S.; Park, S.; Yoon, H.N.; Lee, H.K. Carbonation of calcium sulfoaluminate cement blended with blast furnace slag. *Cement Concr. Compos.* **2021**, *118*, 103918. [CrossRef]
29. Le Saoût, G.; Lothenbach, B.; Hori, A.; Higuchi, T.; Winnefeld, F. Hydration of Portland cement with additions of calcium sulfoaluminates. *Cement Concr. Res.* **2013**, *43*, 81–94. [CrossRef]
30. Juenger, M.C.; Winnefeld, F.; Provis, J.L.; Ideker, J.H. Advances in alternative cementitious binders. *Cement Concr. Res.* **2011**, *41*, 1232–1243. [CrossRef]
31. Meng, K.; Cui, C.; Liang, Z.; Li, H.; Pei, H. A new approach for longitudinal vibration of a large-diameter floating pipe pile in visco-elastic soil considering the three-dimensional wave effects. *Comput. Geotech.* **2020**, *128*, 103840. [CrossRef]
32. Quillin, K. Performance of belite–sulfoaluminate cements. *Cement Concr. Res.* **2001**, *31*, 1341–1349. [CrossRef]
33. Guotang, Z.; Wei, S.; Guotao, Y.; Li, P.; Degou, C.; Jinyang, J.; Hao, H. Mechanism of cement on the performance of cement stabilized aggregate for high speed railway roadbed. *Constr. Build. Mater.* **2017**, *144*, 347–356. [CrossRef]
34. Michel, M.; Georgin, J.F.; Ambroise, J.; Péra, J. The influence of gypsum ratio on the mechanical performance of slag cement accelerated by calcium sulfoaluminate cement. *Constr. Build. Mater.* **2011**, *25*, 1298–1304. [CrossRef]
35. Glasser, F.P.; Zhang, L. High-performance cement matrices based on calcium sulfoaluminate–belite compositions. *Cement Concr. Res.* **2001**, *31*, 1881–1886. [CrossRef]
36. Gastaldi, D.; Paul, G.; Marchese, L.; Irico, S.; Boccaleri, E.; Mutke, S.; Buzzi, L.; Canonico, F. Hydration products in sulfoaluminate cements: Evaluation of amorphous phases by XRD/solid-state NMR. *Cement Concr. Res.* **2016**, *90*, 162–173. [CrossRef]
37. Vinoth, G.; Moon, S.W.; Moon, J.; Ku, T. Early strength development in cement-treated sand using low-carbon rapid-hardening cements. *Soils Found.* **2018**, *58*, 1200–1211. [CrossRef]
38. Li, J.; Chang, J. Effect of crystal/amorphous ratio on mechanical properties in a C4A3 $-C2S hydration system with or without gypsum addition. *Constr. Build. Mater.* **2019**, *208*, 36–45. [CrossRef]
39. Lan, W.; Glasser, F.P. Hydration of calcium sulphoaluminate cements. *Adv. Cement Res.* **1996**, *8*, 127–134. [CrossRef]
40. Tang, S.W.; Zhu, H.G.; Li, Z.J.; Chen, E.; Shao, H.Y. Hydration stage identification and phase transformation of calcium sulfoaluminate cement at early age. *Constr. Build. Mater.* **2015**, *75*, 11–18. [CrossRef]
41. Subramanian, S.; Khan, Q.; Ku, T. Strength development and prediction of calcium sulfoaluminate treated sand with optimized gypsum for replacing OPC in ground improvement. *Constr. Build. Mater.* **2019**, *202*, 308–318. [CrossRef]
42. Rakhimova, N.R. Recent advances in blended alkali-activated cements: A review. *Eur. J. Environ. Civil Eng.* **2020**, *5*, 1–23. [CrossRef]
43. Ngole, V.M.; Totolo, O.; Ekosse, G.E. Physico-chemical and mineralogical characterisation of subsurface sediments around Gaborone Landfill, Botswana. *J. Appl. Sci. Environ. Manag.* **2004**, *8*, 49–53. [CrossRef]
44. Morin, V.; Termkhajornkit, P.; Huet, B.; Pham, G. Impact of quantity of anhydrite, water to binder ratio, fineness on kinetics and phase assemblage of belite-ye'elimite-ferrite cement. *Cem. Concr. Res.* **2017**, *99*, 8–17. [CrossRef]

*Article*

# Towards More Sustainable Materials for Geo-Environmental Engineering: The Case of Geogrids

**Alessio Cislaghi [1,2,*], Paolo Sala [1], Gigliola Borgonovo [3], Claudio Gandolfi [1] and Gian Battista Bischetti [1,2]**

1 Department of Agricultural and Environmental Sciences (DiSAA), University of Milan, Via Celoria 2, 20133 Milan, Italy; paolo.sala@unimi.it (P.S.); claudio.gandolfi@unimi.it (C.G.); bischetti@unimi.it (G.B.B.)
2 Centre of Applied Studies for the Sustainable Management and Protection of Mountain Areas (Ge.S.Di.Mont), University of Milan, Via Morino 8, Edolo, 25048 Brescia, Italy
3 Department of Food, Environmental and Nutritional Sciences, University of Milan, Via Mangiagalli 25, 20133 Milan, Italy; gigliola.borgonovo@unimi.it
* Correspondence: alessio.cislaghi@unimi.it; Tel.: +39-02-503-16903

**Abstract:** Plastic materials are widely used in geotechnical engineering, especially as geosynthetics. The use of plastic-based products involves serious environmental risks caused by their degradation. Innovative research has been focusing on biodegradable polymers of natural origin, especially on poly(lactic acid) (PLA), to reduce the use of plastics. This study aims to explore the potentiality of biopolymers for the production of geogrids, measuring the chemical and mechanical characteristics of raw materials and of prototype samples, similar to those available on the market. First, chemical composition and optical purity were determined by hydrogen nuclear magnetic resonance ($^1$H-NMR) and polarimetry. Furthermore, samples of uniaxial and biaxial geogrids were custom-molded using a professional 3D printer. Mechanical properties were measured both on the filament and on the prototype geogrids. The maximum tensile resistance was 6.76 kN/m for the neat-PLA filament and 10.14 kN/m for uniaxial prototype geogrids produced with PLA-based polymer mixed with titanium dioxide. PLA-based materials showed higher tensile properties than polypropylene (PP), the most common petroleum derivative. Conversely, such biomaterials seem to be more brittle and with scarce elongation rate respect PP. Nonetheless, these results are encouraging and can support the use of PLA-based materials for innovative biodegradable geosynthetics production, especially if used in combination with live plants.

**Keywords:** geosynthetics; poly(lactic acid); biopolymers; geogrids; tensile strength



**Citation:** Cislaghi, A.; Sala, P.; Borgonovo, G.; Gandolfi, C.; Bischetti, G.B. Towards More Sustainable Materials for Geo-Environmental Engineering: The Case of Geogrids. *Sustainability* **2021**, *13*, 2585. https://doi.org/10.3390/su13052585

Academic Editor: Giuseppe Cardile

Received: 22 January 2021
Accepted: 24 February 2021
Published: 28 February 2021



## 1. Introduction

In recent years, the European Union (EU) has developed a new economic paradigm to foster the challenge of sustainability: a Circular Economy approach instead of the classical Linear Economy [1]. A specific focus is on the plastics that are identified as a priority and committed itself to "prepare a strategy addressing the challenges posed by plastics throughout the value chain and taking into account their entire life-cycle". In 2015, the EU plastic demand was 49 millions of tons, about 20%of which for the Construction and Demolition (CaD) sector, which is one of the most challenging fields for reaching the Circular Economy Strategy objectives [2–4]. The main result of this political effort is that many European countries have implemented a framework that leads to a recycling rate of up to 90% as early as the end of 2016. However, this will not be enough because the European Commission is working on a revision of the essential requirements for the use of plastics in CaD to ensure by 2030, all plastics will be reusable or easily recycled. Plastics in CaD are mainly used to produce geosynthetics, i.e., polymeric products used in contact with soil or rock and/or other geotechnical materials and mainly applied in civil and environmental engineering. This term covers a wide range of products such as geotextiles, geomembranes, geogrids, geonets, geocomposites, etc. [5].

Most geosynthetics are fabricated from petroleum-derived polymers such as the polyolefin and polyester family. Polypropylene (PP) covers almost the whole total production (approximately 90%), whereas polyethylene (PE) accounts for the remaining part [5,6]. In the last 7 decades, the scientific effort has been focusing on the mechanical properties to make these materials more resistant to degradation by environmental stressors (e.g., air, ultra-violet (UV) radiation, bacteria) developing mineral fiber reinforced composites and using additives to improve their stability. Thus, for many applications, biodegradability was an undesirable property, because the manufactured products must guarantee long lifespan, low cost, and mechanical properties that ensure great effectiveness. However, this purpose inevitably drove to a clash with the ecological safety. In fact, polymers are heavily subject to a wide range of degradation processes. Over time and under common environmental conditions, plastic composites may degrade into micro-plastics particles (below 5 mm), which persist into the soil and cause negative environmental effects [7]. Moreover, another threat for the environment is the leaching of additives from the composites. This process is particularly complex because many factors influence the loss of additives, such as UV radiation, humidity, temperature and product thickness [8].

Thus, since the last decade, there has promptly been an increasing interest for the natural and biodegradable materials as the biopolymers to replace the synthetic ones in the worldwide market. This considerable interest in biopolymers is associated with an increase of environmental awareness that has led to the scientific and industrial community to search for a good and cost-effective alternative to the conventional materials in several engineering applications [9].

Among the fully biodegradable polymers, the poly(lactic acid) or polylactide (PLA) is certainty the most promising [10]. PLA is a thermoplastic, high-strength and high-modulus polymer [11,12] that has already used on large-scale production and commercialized for a wide range of fields such as food technology, medical engineering, pharmaceutical, packaging and agriculture thanks to its huge versatility [13]. Such biopolymer ensures several advantages in terms of sustainability and eco-compatibility: (i) PLA derives from renewable agriculture-based resources [14]; (ii) PLA decomposes into non-toxic substances, as water, carbon dioxide and humus [9,15] (iii) PLA degrades quite slowly [16]; and (iv) PLA is recyclable and compostable [17]. In addition, neat-PLA has been reinforced with a wide variety of natural fibers such as bamboo, banana, coir, cotton, flax, hemp, jute, kenaf, ramie, sisal, etc. [18,19], and is actually used for numerous applications in automotive, aerospace, construction, civil and the sports and leisure sectors [20–22]. Nevertheless, these biopolymers are not yet adopted in geotechnical and geo-environmental engineering, even if few studies focused on geocomposites products [23,24].

In this context, the present study aims to explore the potentiality and the possibility to use biodegradable polymers, even enhanced with natural fibers, to replace the common petroleum-derivatives polymers in the production of geosynthetics for geo-environmental and geotechnical applications. For pursuing the main objective, this research joins a detailed literature review with specific laboratory measurements to provide a comprehensive and integrated framework for assessing the usability in function of the geo-environmental application. Specific purposes are:

- to explore the market of PLA-based materials and to analyze the recent scientific research aiming at developing innovative bioplastics. The state-of-the-art will provide a complete spectrum of the availability/progress of technology on this kind of materials and the most common applications;
- to produce prototype samples with standard geometry using biopolymers already available on the market and to repeat the chemical and mechanical characterization of these samples;
- to compare the prototype samples produced with different materials analyzing advantages and disadvantage.

## 2. Materials and Methods

### *2.1. State-of-the-Art: Neat-PLA and PLA-Based Materials*

PLA is a linear aliphatic thermoplastic polyester derived from lactic acid, one of the simplest chiral molecules, obtained by the fermentation of renewable and biodegradable plant species, such as corn or rice starch and sugar feedstock [25]. Lactic acid exists in form of two different stereo isomers: L- and D-lactic acid; however, when lactic acid is produced by fermentation, it is largely composed by L-isomer (PLLA) for 99.5%, whereas by D-isomer for 0.5% [18]. From lactic acid, PLA can be produced through different processes: direct condensation, azeotropic dehydrative condensation or ring-opening polymerization [26].

Physical and mechanical properties of neat-PLA are related to its composition (i.e., isomers), processing temperature, annealing, time and molecular weight [27]. Hardness, stiffness, crease, and melting points are linked to the crystallization behavior, which in turn depends on the stereochemistry and thermal history. Among all factors influencing the mechanical properties of neat-PLA, the polymerization process does not apparently cause significant variations [11]. Such mechanical properties have been largely investigated since the late 1990s, thus large amount of data is available from scientific literature, and producer's technical sheets (Table 1). On average, neat-PLA has good mechanical properties: a tensile strength (TS) from 23 to 70 MPa, a tensile modulus or Young's modulus (YM) from 2.3 to 3.8 GPa, and an elongation at break (EL) about 4%. Such variability mainly depends on the polymer characteristics, such as molecular weight and specific gravity. Since the neat-PLA cannot always meet all the requirements for different fields, a common solution consists of incorporating natural fibers for improving specific properties [28–33]. However, a significant gap appears when comparing the measurements of mechanical properties on the neat-PLA with PLA blended with natural fibers, especially in terms of data availability. Most of studies have been recently carried out since a decade ago and have been summarized in Table 2.

The results of these studies underlined how the mechanical properties of the biocomposites can be significantly altered by constituent structures, contents, and production process. In several cases, the addition of natural fibers to neat-PLA improved the tensile resistance of the polymer up to 80–100% (Figure 1). Plackett et al. (2003) [34] and Ben and Kihara (2007) [35] observed an increase of TS from 55 up to more than 100 MPa reinforcing neat-PLA with jute fibers and kenaf fibers, respectively. Excellent improvement of mechanical resistance from 7 to 17 MPa occurred for a neat-PLA blended with corn husk and silane [36]. In addition, satisfactory results, in terms of TS, were obtained in several studies using fibers derived by herbaceous and woody plants. Molding neat-PLA and other natural fibers, Graupner et al. (2009) [37] observed an increase of TS between 37% and 100% using cotton and hemp fibers, according to the fiber content. Similar results were found using the ramie and flax fibers: TS increases of +36% and of +23%, respectively [38,39]. Interesting results were obtained using also fibers derived from synthetic cellulose as rayon. Despite such encouraging results, in other cases, conversely, fiber addition to neat-PLA led to a decrease of tensile strength if compared with pure polymer, for example wood-flour addition decreased PLA TS from 67 MPa to 40–57 MPa [40]. Also blends with milkweed, lesquerella, or cuphea were not successful in enhancing mechanical properties of PLA.

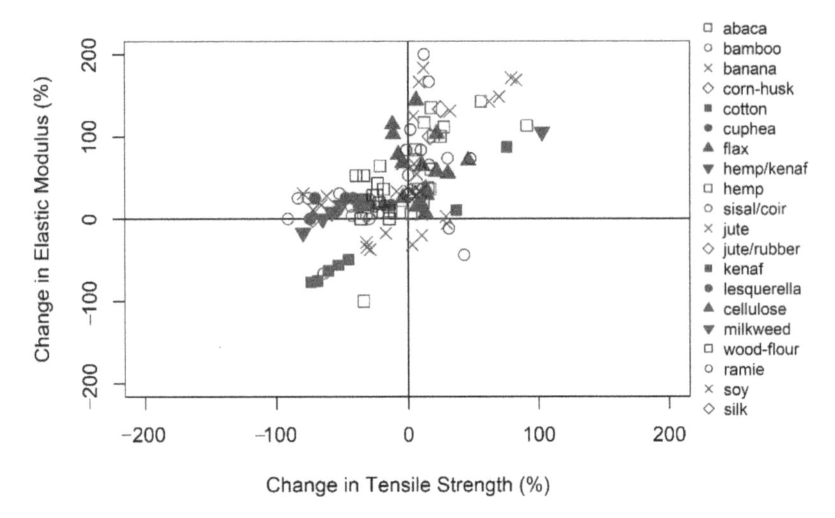


**Figure 1.** Change in percent in terms of Tensile Strength and Elastic Modulus measured between neat-PLA and PLA-based materials.

**Table 1.** Physical and mechanical characteristics of neat-PLA [41]. SG is the specific gravity, EL is the elongation at break, TS is the tensile strength and YM is the Young's modulus.

| Supplier and Product | Form | Process | SG (g/cc) | EL (%) | TS (MPa) | YM (GPa) |
|---|---|---|---|---|---|---|
| NatureWorks Biopolymer 3D850 | Filament | Extrusion-Injection molding | 1.24 | 3.3 | 50.0 | 2.3 |
| NatureWorks Biopolymer 3D870 | Filament | Extrusion-Injection molding | 1.22 | 4.0 | 40.0 | 2.9 |
| NatureWorks Biopolymer 4043D | Filament | Extrusion-Injection molding | 1.24 | 6.0 | 53.0 | 3.6 |
| NatureWorks Biopolymer 4032D | Resin | Extrusion-Injection molding | 1.24 | 6.0 | 53.0 | 3.5 |
| NatureWorks Biopolymer 4042D | Film | Melt blending-Compression molding | 1.25 | 3.6 | 56.3 | 3.3–3.8 |
| colorFabb PLA Economy | Filament | Extrusion-Injection molding | 1.20–1.30 | 6.0 | 45.0 | 3.4 |
| colorFabb SteelFill | Filament | Extrusion-Injection molding | 1.13 | 1.0–3.0 | 23.0 | - |
| NatureWorks Biopolymer 2000D | Film | Extrusion-Thermoforming | 1.25 | 6.0 | 53.0 | 3.5 |
| NatureWorks Biopolymer 3010D | Film | Extrusion-Injection molding | 1.21 | 2.5 | 48.0 | - |
| NatureWorks Biopolymer 2002D | Resin | Extrusion-Injection molding | 1.24 | 2.0 | 60.0 | 3.5 |
| NatureWorks Biopolymer 2002D | Resin | Extrusion-Blown molding | 1.24 | 2.1 | 34.6 | 3.5 |
| NatureWorks Biopolymer 4042D | Film | Melt blending-Compression molding | 1.25 | 7.4 | 70.2 | 3.3 |
| NatureWorks Biopolymer 4042D | Film | Extrusion-Injection molding | 1.25 | 1.0 | 38.0 | 3.8 |
| NatureWorks Biopolymer 2002D | Resin | Melt blending-Compression molding | 1.24 | 4.5 | 55.0 | 3.5 |
| NatureWorks Biopolymer 4032D | Resin | Extrusion-Injection molding | 1.24 | 5.0 | 65.0 | 3.5 |
| NatureWorks Biopolymer 2000D | Film | Casting (chloroform) | 1.25 | 7.9 | 24.8 | 3.5 |

**Table 2.** Main characteristics of PLA-based composites collected from the literature. C is the fiber content, PT is the processing temperature, TS is the tensile strength, YM is the Young's modulus, and EL is the elongation at break. In bold font, the measurements related to neat-PLA. The values in bold refer to neat-PLA.

| Reinforced-PLA | Processing | C (%) | PT (°C) | TS (MPa) | YM (GPa) | EL (%) |
|---|---|---|---|---|---|---|
| **neat-PLA** blended with jute fibers (*Corchorus capsularis*) [34] | film-stacking | **0** | **190** | **55.0** | **3.5** | **2.1** |
| | | 40 | 180 | 72.7 | 8.1 | 1.5 |
| | | 40 | 190 | 89.3 | 8.5 | 1.8 |
| | | 40 | 200 | 93.5 | 8.7 | 1.6 |
| | | 40 | 210 | 100.5 | 9.4 | 1.6 |
| | | 40 | 220 | 98.5 | 9.5 | 1.5 |
| **neat-PLA** blended with cuphea oil-seeds (*Cuphea viscosissima* × *C. lanceolata*) [42] | twin-screw extrusion | **0** | **160** | **72.0** | **1.2** | **14.5** |
| | | 8 | 156 | 62.6 | 1.4 | 7.8 |
| | | 15 | 153 | 51.4 | 1.4 | 6.1 |
| | | 22 | 155 | 41.9 | 1.5 | 5.4 |
| | | 30 | 150 | 37.9 | 1.5 | 7.9 |
| | | 45 | 148 | 21.2 | 1.5 | 4.6 |
| **neat-PLA** blended with lesquerella oil-seeds (*Lesquerella fenderli*) [42] | twin-screw extrusion | **0** | **160** | **72.0** | **1.2** | **14.5** |
| | | 8 | 156 | 58.9 | 1.4 | 8.8 |
| | | 15 | 156 | 48.9 | 1.4 | 7.6 |
| | | 22 | 155 | 45.6 | 1.4 | 5.4 |
| | | 30 | 154 | 32.2 | 1.3 | 7.9 |
| | | 45 | 149 | 18.5 | 1.2 | 4.6 |
| **neat-PLA** blended with milkweed oil-seeds (*Asclepias syriaca* and *Asclepias speciose*) [42] | twin-screw extrusion | **0** | **160** | **72.0** | **1.2** | **14.5** |
| | | 8 | 154 | 48.1 | 1.5 | 20.1 |
| | | 15 | 155 | 35.2 | 1.4 | 34.6 |
| | | 22 | 155 | 30.3 | 1.3 | 30.4 |
| | | 30 | 155 | 25.3 | 1.2 | 23.1 |
| | | 45 | 155 | 14.7 | 1.0 | 14.3 |
| **neat-PLA** [37] | compression molding | 0 | **160–170** | **30.1** | **3.8** | **0.8** |
| **neat-PLA** blended with cotton fibers (*Gossypium* sp.) [37] | | 40 | 160–170 | 41.2 | 4.2 | 3.1 |
| **neat-PLA** blended with kenaf fibers (*Hibiscus cannabinus*) [37] | | 40 | 160–170 | 52.9 | 7.1 | 1.1 |
| **neat-PLA** blended with hemp fibers (*Cannabis sativa*) [37] | | 40 | 160–170 | 57.5 | 8.1 | 1.2 |
| **neat-PLA** blended with hemp fibers (*Cannabis sativa*) and kenaf fibers (*Hibiscus cannabinus*) [37] | | 20/20 | 160–170 | 61.0 | 7.8 | 1.2 |
| **neat-PLA** blended with ramie fibers (*Boehmeria nivea*) [32,39] | - | **0** | **170** | **45.2** | **2.6** | **1.2** |
| | compression molding | 30 | 170 | 52.5 | 4.3 | 3.2 |
| | | 30 ** | 170 | 66.8 | 4.5 | 4.8 |
| | twin-screw extrusion | 30 | 170 | 59.3 | 2.3 | 4.1 |
| **neat-PLA** blended with bamboo fibers [43] | - | **0** | **170** | **61.9** | **3.4** | |
| | | 35 | 170 | 80.6 | 5.9 | |
| | | 35 | 170 | 61.9 | 5.2 | |
| **neat-PLA** blended with hemp fibers (*Cannabis sativa*) [44] | compression molding | **0** | **170** | **35.0** | **3.5** | **6.0** |
| | | 30 ** | 170 | 39.3 | 7.6 | |
| | | 30 | 170 | 41.1 | 5.6 | |
| | | 40 ** | 170 | 54.6 | 8.5 | |
| | | 40 | 170 | 44.6 | 7.4 | |
| | | 50 ** | 170 | 41.8 | 7.0 | |
| | | 50 | 170 | 43.7 | 7.0 | |

**Table 2.** *Cont.*

| Reinforced-PLA | Processing | C (%) | PT (°C) | TS (MPa) | YM (GPa) | EL (%) |
|---|---|---|---|---|---|---|
| **neat-PLA** blended with jute fibers (*Corchorus capsularis*) [45] | compression molding | **0** | **180** | **34.6** | **3.5** | **2.1** |
| | | 5 | 200 | 23.6 | 2.5 | 6.4 |
| | | 10 | 200 | 38.2 | 2.8 | 5.7 |
| | | 15 | 200 | 44.8 | 3.3 | 5.8 |
| | | 5 | 210 | 24.6 | 2.2 | 5.6 |
| | | 10 | 210 | 35.7 | 2.4 | 5.6 |
| | | 15 | 210 | 44.6 | 3.6 | 5.2 |
| | | 5 | 220 | 23.7 | 2.3 | 5.6 |
| | | 10 | 220 | 28.7 | 2.9 | 5.2 |
| | | 15 | 220 | 38.1 | 3.7 | 5.4 |
| **neat-PLA** blended with flax fibers (*Linum usitastissimum* L. and *Linum Linacea*) [38] | compression and injection | **0** | **180** | **44.5** | **3.1** | |
| | | 10 | 180 | 42.7 | 3.9 | |
| | | 20 | 180 | 49.2 | 5.1 | |
| | | 30 | 180 | 54.2 | 6.3 | |
| **neat-PLA** blended with rayon fibers [38] | | 10 | 180 | 50.4 | 3.3 | |
| | | 20 | 180 | 50.8 | 4.0 | |
| | | 30 | 180 | 58.0 | 4.8 | |
| **neat-PLA** [46] | single-screw extrusion and injection | **0** | | **63.0** | **3.4** | |
| **neat-PLA** blended with abaca fibers (*Musa textilis*) [46] | | 30 | 180 | 74.0 | 8.0 | |
| **neat-PLA** blended with man-made cellulose fibers [46] | | 30 | 180 | 92.0 | 5.8 | |
| **neat-PLA** blended with flax fibers (*Linum usitatissimum*) [47] | twin-screw extrusion and compression molding | **0** | **190** | **50.0** | **3.4** | **2.0** |
| | | 30 | 190 | 53.0 | 8.3 | 1.0 |
| | | 40 | 190 | 44.0 | 7.3 | 0.9 |
| **neat-PLA** blended with banana fibers (*Musa indica*) [48] | compression molding | **0** | **190** | **38** | **3.6** | **2.9** |
| | | 10 ** | 190 | 10.6 | 4.0 | 1.5 |
| | | 20 ** | 190 | 13.0 | 4.2 | 1.1 |
| | | 30 ** | 190 | 14.6 | 4.6 | 1.1 |
| | | 40 ** | 190 | 7.8 | 4.7 | 0.9 |
| **neat-PLA** blended with banana fibers (*Musa indica*) [49] | compression molding | **0** | | **39.3** | **1.2** | **2.5** |
| | | 20 | 185 | 46.3 | 6.6 | 0.2 |
| **neat-PLA** blended with hemp fibers (*Cannabis sativa*) [50] | hot pressing | **0** | | **58.8** | **2.5** | |
| | | 6 | 170 | 65.7 | 3.0 | |
| | | 20 | 170 | 68.7 | 3.4 | |
| **neat-PLA** blended with kenaf fibers (*Hibiscus cannabinus*) [35] | hot pressing | **0** | | **55.4** | **1.4** | **4.8** |
| | | 38 | 185 | 111.6 | 5.9 | 2.7 |
| **neat-PLA** blended with bamboo fibers [51] | film-stacking | **0** | | **54.3** | **3.2** | **5.3** |
| | | 50 | 160 | 77.58 | 1.8 | 14.6 |
| **neat-PLA** blended with wood-flour [40] | hot pressing | **0** | | **67.4** | **2.1** | **5.1** |
| | | 10 | 200 | 57.5 | 2.3 | 3.4 |
| | | 20 | 200 | 52.5 | 2.5 | 2.9 |
| | | 30 | 200 | 51.4 | 2.7 | 2.4 |
| | | 40 | 200 | 49.3 | 2.7 | 2.5 |
| | | 50 | 200 | 44.8 | 3.2 | 1.9 |
| | | 60 | 200 | 40.7 | 3.2 | 1.8 |

Table 2. *Cont.*

| Reinforced-PLA | Processing | C (%) | PT (°C) | TS (MPa) | YM (GPa) | EL (%) |
|---|---|---|---|---|---|---|
| **neat-PLA** blended with silk fibers [21] | twin-screw extrusion | **0** | **180** | **70.73** | **3.2** | **5.5** |
| | | 5 | 180 | 70.6 | 4.1 | 3.8 |
| **neat-PLA** blended with kenaf fibers (*Hibiscus cannabinus*) [52] | hot pressing | **0** | **180** | **58.2** | **8.7** | **1.9** |
| | | 10 | 180 | 23.0 | 3.2 | |
| | | 20 | 180 | 27.3 | 3.8 | |
| | | 30 | 180 | 31.9 | 4.4 | 0.7 |
| | | 40 | 180 | 18.2 | 2.1 | |
| | | 50 | 180 | 15.3 | 2.0 | |
| **neat-PLA** blended with bamboo fibers [53] | compression molding | **0** | | **49.8** | **2.6** | **3.1** |
| | | 10 | 180 | 35.1 | 2.6 | 2.3 |
| | | 20 | 180 | 34.1 | 2.7 | 2.4 |
| | | 30 | 180 | 28.6 | 2.7 | 2.6 |
| | | 40 | 180 | 28.2 | 3.0 | 1.8 |
| | | 50 | 180 | 23.8 | 3.4 | 1.6 |
| **neat-PLA** [54] | injection | **0** | **160** | **51.9** | **1.1** | **8.8** |
| | compression molding | 0 | 160 | 55.7 | 0.6 | 15.5 |
| **neat-PLA** blended with jute fibers (*Corchorus capsularis*) [54] | injection | **20** | **160** | **55.3** | **1.7** | **4.7** |
| | compression molding | 20 | 160 | 50.8 | 0.8 | 8.2 |
| **neat-PLA** blended with jute fibers (*Corchorus capsularis*) and natural rubber [54] | injection | **20/10** | **160** | **17.2** | **1.2** | **2.3** |
| | compression molding | 20/10 | 160 | 15.4 | 0.6 | 9.4 |
| **neat-PLA** [36] | single-screw extrusion | **0** | | **7.2** | **0.5** | |
| **neat-PLA** blended with corn husk [36] | | 0 ** | 160 | 13.7 | 0.3 | |
| | | 1.5 ** | 160 | 15.0 | 0.4 | |
| | | 2.5 ** | 160 | 14.2 | 0.4 | |
| | | 3.5 ** | 160 | 13.9 | 0.4 | |
| **neat-PLA** blended with corn husk and treated with silane [36] | | 3/1.5 | 160 | 15.0 | 0.4 | |
| | | 5/1.5 | 160 | 17.1 | 0.7 | |
| | | 7/1.5 | 160 | 16.0 | 0.6 | |
| | | 10/1.5 | 160 | 14.0 | 0.4 | |
| **neat-PLA** [55] | - | **0** | | **67.3** | **3.7** | **6.6** |
| **neat-PLA** blended with flax fibers (*Linum usitatissimum*) [55] | | 20 | 190–230 | 64.4 | 6.2 | 6.2 |
| **neat-PLA** blended with hemp fibers (*Cannabis sativa*) [55] | | 20 | 190–230 | 71.0 | 6.8 | 5.8 |
| **neat-PLA** [56] | twin-screw extrusion | **0** | | **35.1** | **2.5** | |
| **neat-PLA** blended with hemp fibers (*Cannabis sativa*) [56] | | 10 ** | 160 | 37.7 | 3.4 | |
| | | 20 ** | 160 | 28.5 | 3.4 | |
| | | 30 ** | 160 | 23.2 | | |
| **neat-PLA** blended with harakeke fibers (*Phormium tenax*) [56] | | 10 ** | 170 | 33.5 | 2.7 | |
| | | 20 ** | 170 | 36.8 | 4.3 | |
| | | 30 ** | 170 | 27.6 | 4.1 | |
| **neat-PLA** blended with Osage orange fibers (*Maclura pomifera*) [42] | single-screw extrusion | **0** | | **57.5** | **0.6** | **18.6** |
| | | 10 | 150–170 | 49.2 | 0.6 | 11.4 |
| | | 25 | 150–170 | 36.9 | 0.6 | 8.0 |
| **neat-PLA** blended with flax fibers (*Linum usitatissimum*) [57] | injection | **0** | | **60.1** | **3.6** | **2.4** |
| | | 20 | 220 | 55.5 | 6.4 | 1.4 |
| | | 30 | 220 | 53.1 | 7.3 | 1.1 |

**Table 2.** *Cont.*

| Reinforced-PLA | Processing | C (%) | PT (°C) | TS (MPa) | YM (GPa) | EL (%) |
|---|---|---|---|---|---|---|
| **neat-PLA** [58] | hot pressing | 0 | | **45.3** | **1.2** | |
| **neat-PLA** blended with jute fibers (*Corchorus capsularis*) [58] | | 10 | 170 | 47.3 | 2.0 | |
| | | 20 | 170 | 49.1 | 3.2 | |
| | | 30 | 170 | 50.6 | 3.4 | |
| | | 40 | 170 | 47.1 | 2.7 | |
| | | 50 | 170 | 43.3 | 2.0 | |
| **neat-PLA** blended with ramie fibers (*Boehmeria nivea*) [58] | | 10 | 170 | 49.7 | 2.2 | |
| | | 20 | 170 | 50.8 | 3.6 | |
| | | 30 | 170 | 52.5 | 3.2 | |
| | | 40 | 170 | 46.1 | 2.5 | |
| | | 50 | 170 | 44.7 | 2.2 | |
| **neat-PLA** blended with wood-flour [59] | injection | 0 | | **67.9** | **4.2** | **4.4** |
| | | 7.5 | 160–170 | 54.8 | 4.5 | 2.8 |
| | | 15 | 160–170 | 52.0 | 6.0 | 2.0 |
| **neat-PLA** blended with hemp fibers (*Cannabis sativa*) [60] | twin-screw extrusion | 0 | | **51.4** | **3.2** | **4.5** |
| | | 3 | 170–180 | 52.5 | 3.4 | 4.1 |
| | | 3 ** | 170–180 | 55.7 | 3.8 | 3.1 |
| | | 6 | 170–180 | 53.2 | 3.8 | 2.9 |
| | | 6 ** | 170–180 | 59.3 | 4.4 | 1.8 |
| **neat-PLA** blended with microfibrillated cellulose [61] | hot pressing | 0 | **164** | **57.7** | **3.3** | **6.8** |
| | | 3 | 164 | 61.4 | 3.8 | 2.7 |
| | | 5 | 164 | 63.4 | 3.9 | 2.5 |
| | | 10 | 164 | 65.4 | 4.5 | 2.2 |
| | | 20 | 164 | 70.2 | 5.2 | 1.9 |
| **neat-PLA** blended with toddy palm fibers (*Borassus Flabellifer*) [62] | compression molding | 0 | | **52.7** | | **2.0** |
| | | 30 | 180 | 25.0 | 2.0 | 9.1 |
| **neat-PLA** blended with hybrid sisal and coir fibers [63] | hot compression molding | 0 | | **53.6** | **1.3** | |
| | | 10 | 180 | 41.7 | 1.4 | |
| | | 20 | 180 | 39.9 | 1.5 | |
| | | 30 | 180 | 38.0 | 1.6 | |
| | | 40 | 180 | 33.6 | 1.5 | |
| **neat-PLA** blended with hybrid sisal and coir fibers [64] | hot pressing | 0 | | **23.5** | **1.2** | **2.3** |
| | | 5 | 180 | 3.9 | 1.5 | 0.4 |
| | | 10 | 180 | 2.1 | 1.2 | 0.5 |
| | | 20 | 180 | 5.7 | 1.5 | 0.8 |
| | | 30 | 180 | 8.4 | 0.4 | 3.3 |

** indicates that the biomaterials were alkali-treated.

### 2.2. Tested Biomaterials

This study conducted a series of analysis on 6 different biomaterials and 2 petroleum-derivates. The selection was carried out considering the availability on the market, adaptability for the 3D printing process (i.e., consumables for 3D printers), eco-compatibility, and slow degradation rate. This choice allowed to produce uniaxial and biaxial prototype geogrids using a 3D printing processes. Based on the requirements, a total of 6 materials in form of 1.75 mm diameter filament were selected:

- neat-PLA filament (n-PLA; PLA, Orbi-Tech© company, Leichlingen, Germany);
- neat-PLA filament containing co-polyesters and non-toxic additives to enhance 3D printing performance (ad-PLA; PLA NX2, Extrudr© company, Lauterach, Austria);
- neat-PLA filament containing polymeric additives and titanium dioxide for improving the strength performance under thermal treatment (ht-PLA; HTPLA V3, Proto-Pasta©, Protoplant, Vancouver, WA, USA);

- hemp fibers reinforced-PLA filament containing approximately 20% of raw fibers (h-PLA; HempBioPlastic, Kànesis©, MICA company, Catania, Italy);
- cork fibers reinforced-PLA filament containing approximately 20% of raw fibers (c-PLA; Corkfill, ColorFabb© company, Belfeld, The Netherlands);
- wood fibers reinforced-PLA filament containing approximately 20% of raw fibers (w-PLA; Woodfill, ColorFabb© company, Belfeld, The Netherlands).

Moreover, PP (Renkforce©, Conrad Electronic, Hirschau, Germany) and polyethylene terephthalate glycol PETG (XYZprinting©, Taipei, Taiwan) filaments were tested and used for producing prototype geogrids for a comparison with biopolymer-based filaments and prototype samples.

### 2.3. Chemical and Mechanical Characterization of Biomaterials

A detailed characterization was carried out on the selected biomaterials. First, the chemical characterization of PLA-based samples was obtained through optical purity analysis and $^1$H-NMR spectroscopy to determinate enantiomeric ratio of the two lactic acid stereoisomers composing the PLA-based samples, and their structure. Specific optical rotation ($[\alpha]_D$) was registered with a JASCO P-2000 polarimeter, at 25 °C with a wavelength of 589 nm. PLA-based samples were solubilized in chloroform ($CHCl_3$) at a concentration of 1.00 g/dL. If necessary, some solutions were filtered with polytetrafluoroethylene syringe filters to avoid the insoluble particulate to interfere with the polarimetric analysis. Optical purity was calculated referring to the $[\alpha]_D$ value of pure poly (L-lactic acid). Equation (1) defines the percentage of optical purity (OP):

$$OP(\%) = \frac{[\alpha]_{589}^{25}}{-156} \cdot 100 \quad (1)$$

where $[\alpha]$ is the specific rotation observed and −156 is the specific rotation for L-lactic acid enantiopure PLA, at a concentration of 1 g/dL at 25 °C [65]. NMR spectra were recorded at 25 °C with a Bruker AV 600 spectrometer at 600 MHz. Samples were prepared solubilizing PLA in CDCl3 in a range of concentration of 3–6 mg/mL.

Mechanical tests were performed using a Universal Testing Machine (MTS Criterion Model 44, MTS Systems Corporation, Eden Prairie, MN, USA) equipped with universal clamps (with a distance between the jaws of 10 cm) that avoided sample damage at the clamping points according to ASTM D6637 standard. Tensile force (in N) was exerted by a system of gears at a rate of 10 mm/min and it was measured as a function of the strain by a load cell (F.S. = 5000 N). The tensile force at the point of rupture was taken as the peak load, and TS (MPa) was calculated by dividing the breaking force by the cross-sectional area of the filament (mm$^2$). For model geogrids, TS (kN/m) was calculated by dividing the breaking force by the sample width.

### 2.4. Prototypes Building and Testing

In geotechnical engineering research, the geosynthetics and in particular geogrids have been tested into physical model experiments: from the small-scale and large-scale laboratory tests to full-scale field tests. Certainly, full-scale model tests are more representative of field conditions, but they are very expensive and inevitably present difficulties associated with the model preparation [66,67]. In the literature, small-scale test results are compared to those obtained by full-scale ones [68–70]. Moreover, 3D printing has become a revolutionary technology and has proven to be an important tool for many fields of engineering applications. Thanks to the flexibility of this technology, 3D printers quickly transform theoretical design concepts into prototypes, on which it is possible to verify their feasibility. The pioneering studies that underlined how 3D printing can support geotechnical engineering are recent [71–74]. This technology allows better understanding of the mechanical behavior of innovative elements of geotechnical structures testing materials, geometries, and positions. Recently, Stathas et al. (2017) [74] using this technology, successfully fabricated and tested standard prototypes of model geogrids according to the technical specifications of the geotechnical literature [70,75]. The TS of model geogrids used in 1:N-reinforced soil models must be $1/N^2$ of that of full-scale geogrids when the test is carried out under 1-g condition, or $n/N^2$ of that of prototype (small-scale geogrids) under n-g condition in centrifuge tests. Please note that N represents the scale of a reduced model and n is the level of gravity that the model is subjected to; usually, n is set equal to N [76].

For this study, two model geogrids were designed and tested on a scale of 1:5 so that could be used to investigate the behavior of geosynthetics-reinforced soil structures in $5\times g$ centrifuge models. Uniaxial and biaxial geogrids were designed scaling to 1:5 the standard dimensions of full-scale geogrids available on the market. The prototype samples were produced by a Sharebot NG 2 printer using the manufacturing technology of the fused filament fabrication (a common 3D printing process for thermoplastic materials) and the printer feedstock is a continuous filament. The dimensions of the prototype samples were 50 mm width × 150 mm length, and 0.5 mm thick, with an accuracy of 0.1 mm. Mechanical tests were carried out on 1.75 mm diameter filaments and on 3D printed geogrids samples.

## 3. Results

### 3.1. Chemical and Mechanical Characterization of Biomaterials

The average $[\alpha]_D$ values of samples containing PLA are showed in Table 3. Neat PLA showed a specific rotation value of $-128.70 \pm 1.40^\circ$ that was the highest recorded followed by h-PLA and c-PLA with $-110.05 \pm 1.56^\circ$ and $-107.62 \pm 0.16^\circ$, respectively. In contrast, the lowest $[\alpha]_D$ values were recorded for ht-PLA and ad-PLA, with $-70.75 \pm 1.01^\circ$ and $-35.50 \pm 0.14^\circ$ respectively. Optical purity values, for being calculated on the base of $[\alpha]_D$, presented the same trend: n-PLA showed the highest value of $81.96 \pm 0.52\%$ while ad-PLA the lowest, with $23.50 \pm 0.05\%$.

**Table 3.** Results of chemical properties: specific rotation $[\alpha]_D$ (°) and optical purity OP (%).

| Biomaterial | $[\alpha]_D$ (°) | OP (%) |
|---|---|---|
| n-PLA | $-128.70 \pm 1.40$ | $81.96 \pm 0.52$ |
| ad-PLA | $-35.50 \pm 0.14$ | $23.50 \pm 0.05$ |
| ht-PLA | $-70.75 \pm 1.01$ | $45.73 \pm 0.18$ |
| h-PLA | $-110.05 \pm 1.56$ | $70.54 \pm 1.30$ |
| c-PLA | $-107.62 \pm 0.16$ | $68.63 \pm 0.09$ |
| w-PLA | $-102.17 \pm 0.14$ | $67.47 \pm 0.07$ |

The structure of n-PLA was confirmed by NMR analysis in all the samples. In the protonic spectrum a quartet and a doublet were observed at 5.15 and 1.57 ppm. Those signals are typical of the CH and $CH_3$ groups of the polymeric chain. In the protonic spectrum, a weak quartet at 4.35 ppm was also visible and compatible with the terminal CH. The results obtained by h-PLA $^1H$-NMR spectrum showed other signals in the central region, between 3.3 and 4.5 ppm, and intense high-field peaks, whereas other weak high-field peaks that could refer to compound sugars, were evident at 0.86 ppm (triplet), at 1.23 ppm (singlet) and 1.52 ppm (singlet). Thanks to the filtration process, the protonic spectrum of sample ad-PLA showed higher resolution. Signals compatible with an organic compound part of the solution (about 10%) were detected. In particular, the double triplets resonating at 4.07 and 4.38 could be attributed to methylenic structures of a polyesteric chain (O-$CH_2$-$CH_2$-O-COO-) and the signal at 2.31 ppm could be ascribed to a methylene group adjacent to an esteric group ($CH_2$-COO-). The ht-PLA spectra resulted comparable before and after filtration. The structure of PLA was confirmed but signals compatibles with lactide were detected at 1.7 and 5.0 ppm. No other organic compound was detected. The c-PLA and w-PLA samples showed similar protonic spectra overlapping the quartet signals that were detected at 5.17 and 5.24 ppm. Other signals between 1.3 and 2.7 ppm among with polyesteric chains signals (about 10%) were highlighted.

From the mechanical point of view, the measurements carried out with the tensile tests provided a preliminary characterization of these materials: the results are summarized in Table 4. The filaments of n-PLA showed the most tensile resistant than the others with a TS of 51.93 ± 2.28 MPa. Among the PLA-based polymers, the filaments of the additive-enriched PLA, i.e., ad-PLA and ht-PLA, provided a relevant tensile resistance ranging between 34 MPa to 49 MPa. Conversely, a gap was evident comparing n-PLA and the additive-enriched PLA with the natural fibers reinforced-PLA. In fact, h-PLA, c-PLA, and w-PLA showed an average of TS equal to 23 MPa, 28 MPa, and 29 MPa, respectively.

**Table 4.** Measurements of mechanical properties obtained by tensile tests: tensile strength (TS), Young modulus (YM) and elongation rate (EL).

| Biomaterial | TS (MPa) | YM (GPa) | EL (%) |
|---|---|---|---|
| n-PLA | 51.93 ± 2.28 | 2.70 ± 1.82 | 5.87 ± 2.53 |
| ad-PLA | 34.60 ± 1.00 | 2.89 ± 0.72 | 4.53 ± 0.62 |
| ht-PLA | 47.28 ± 1.72 | 3.44 ± 0.52 | 6.89 ± 1.73 |
| h-PLA | 23.00 ± 4.56 | 3.73 ± 1.01 | 3.08 ± 1.06 |
| c-PLA | 27.58 ± 0.34 | 2.74 ± 0.67 | 3.83 ± 0.15 |
| w-PLA | 28.74 ± 0.58 | 3.37 ± 1.63 | 3.80 ± 0.71 |

### 3.2. *Prototypes Samples Building and Testing*

The prototypes were produced with a Sharebot NG2 3D printer with Fused Deposition Modeling technology overlapping two thin layers of fused material. The extrusion temperatures ranged between 190 and 220 °C although it depends on which biomaterial must be printed. All the prototype samples met the necessary demands of accuracy in dimension variability [74]. In particular, the error was ±0.06 mm along the planar directions, whereas was ±0.0025 mm in thickness. The excellent accuracy did not completely prevent the lack of defects, generally concentrated in the junctions. Figure 2 shows some examples of the prototype samples of geogrids produced using n-PLA and h-PLA.

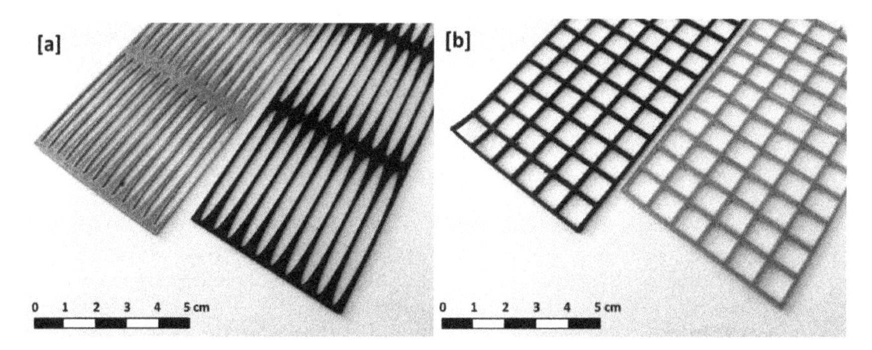


**Figure 2.** Examples of (**a**) uniaxial and (**b**) biaxial prototype geogrids produced using n-PLA (black) and h-PLA (brown) prototype geogrids.

As expected, evident differences were observed conducting tests on uniaxial and biaxial prototype samples. For all materials, the uniaxial geogrids provide a more consistent tensile resistance than the biaxial ones. The increase of TS varies from 48% of the n-PLA to 215% in the case of ad-PLA. Conversely, such difference is attenuated in the case of PETG and PP samples. In terms of TS, good performance was provided by n-PLA and additives-enhanced PLA prototypes. In particular, n-PLA uniaxial geogrids were characterized by an average TS of 6.76 ± 0.19 kN/m and by a pronounced elastic deformation phase (Figure 3). Biaxial samples provided a lower value of TS (4.56 ± 0.75 kN/m) and showed a marked with a strain at break less than 2%.

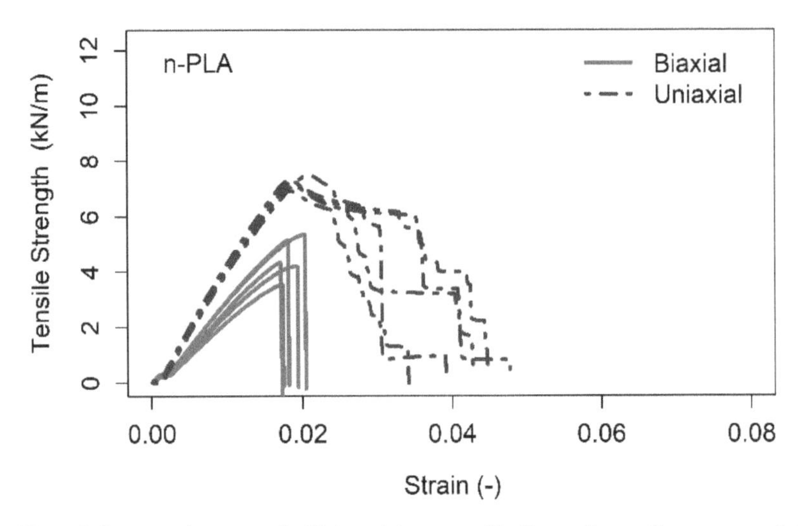


**Figure 3.** Stress-strain curves of n-PLA prototype geogrids: the continuous line corresponds to the biaxial samples, whereas the dotted line to the uniaxial ones.

Considering all the biomaterials, ht-PLA is the more resistant in both uniaxial and biaxial cases with TS values of 10.14 ± 1.50 kN/m and 6.71 ± 0.15 kN/m respectively (Figure 4). However, it was meanwhile the stiffest one. Analyzing the stress-strain curves, the plastic deformation phase seems to be completely absent and the strain at break is slightly more than 2%. In the case of ad-PLA, uniaxial geogrids showed a good tensile resistance with 6.69 ± 1.90 kN/m with an elongation at break up to 8% (Figure 5). This condition represents the best performance in terms of the elongation rate than the other prototypes produced with other biomaterials. Biaxial samples provided a lower TS (2.12 ± 1.26 kN/m) and a significant lower strain at break. Samples of PLA-reinforced with natural fibers yielded lower values in terms of TS and the same strain rate at break, if compared to the neat biomaterial. Uniaxial prototypes made using h-PLA showed a TS of 4.44 ± 1.26 kN/m, while biaxial ones 2.73 ± 1.08 kN/m (Figure 6). The prototypes containing hemp fibers resulted about 35% less resistant and less elastic than the corresponding in neat-PLA. In addition, h-PLA was the worst resistant biomaterial, without showing a relevant improvement in terms of elasticity. Undoubtedly, a certain uncertainty was related to the difficulties for reproducing the geometry of the prototype samples during the 3D printing process. Such fact was probably caused by the extreme stiffness of this biomaterial. Weak resistance was shown by geogrid prototypes produced with w-PLA. They did not provide satisfactory results both in tensile resistance and elasticity, with a recorded TS of 3.5 ± 1.04 kN/m for uniaxial models and 2.84 ± 0.73 kN/m for biaxial ones (strain at break <2%) (Figure 7). Conversely, c-PLA uniaxial geogrids combine a moderate TS with an encouraging strain at break compared to the PLA samples blended with the other natural fibers (hemp and wood blends) (Figure 8). TS was 4.49 ± 1.22 kN/m, whereas the elongation at break was over 8%. Biaxial models produced variable stress-strain curves with lower resistant characteristics: TS was 1.93 ± 0.53 kN/m.

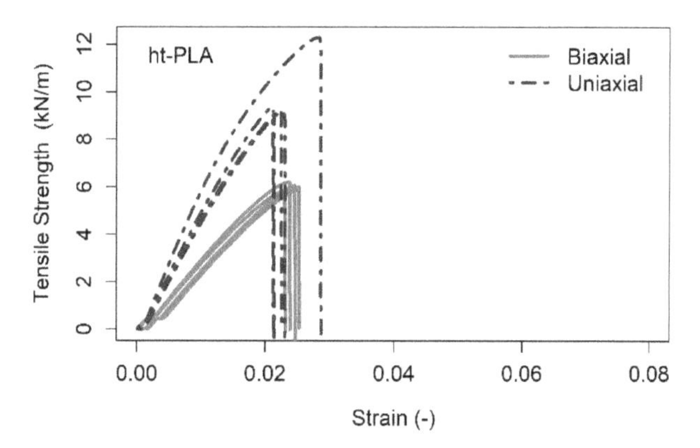


**Figure 4.** Stress-strain curves of ht-PLA prototype geogrids: the continuous line corresponds to the biaxial samples, whereas the dotted line to the uniaxial ones.

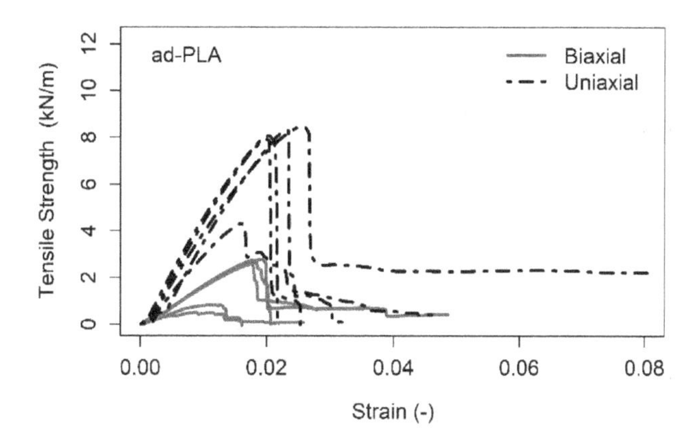


**Figure 5.** Stress-strain curves of ad-PLA prototype geogrids: the continuous line corresponds to the biaxial samples, whereas the dotted line to the uniaxial ones.

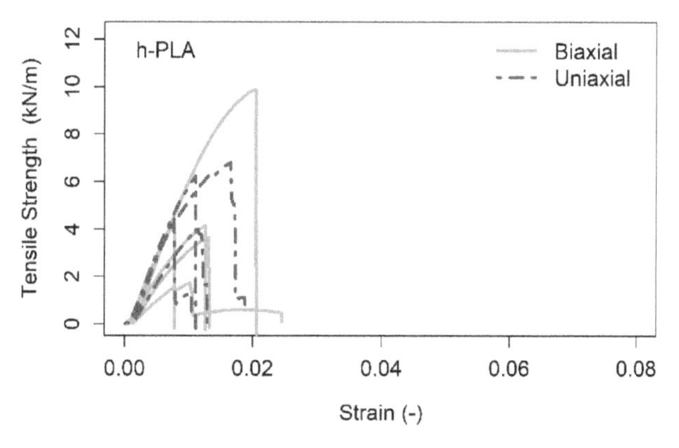


**Figure 6.** Stress-strain curves of h-PLA prototype geogrids: the continuous line corresponds to the biaxial samples, whereas the dotted line to the uniaxial ones.

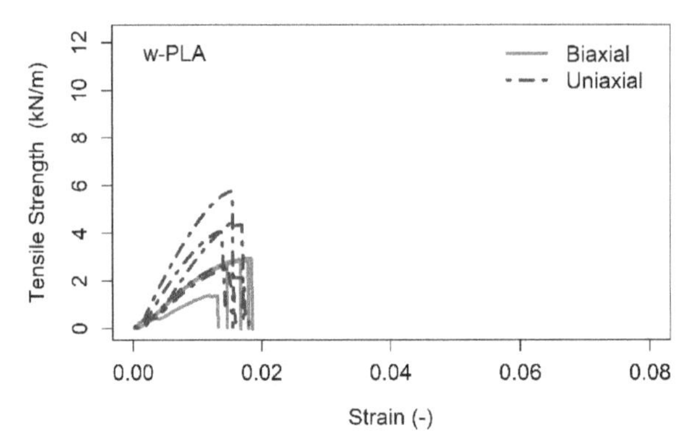


**Figure 7.** Stress-strain curves of w-PLA prototype geogrids: the continuous line corresponds to the biaxial samples, whereas the dotted line to the uniaxial ones.

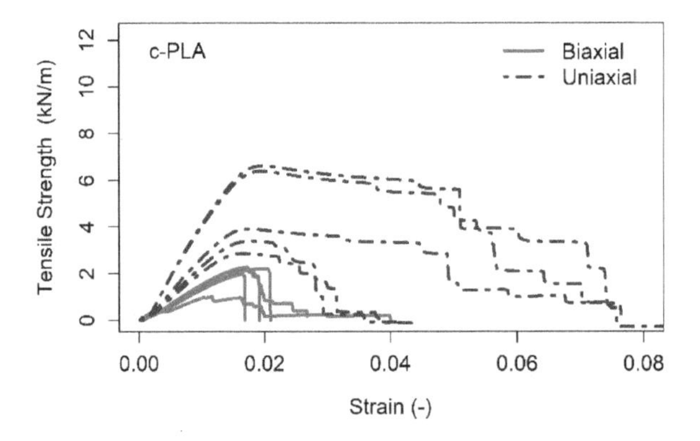


**Figure 8.** Stress-strain curves of c-PLA prototype geogrids: the continuous line corresponds to the biaxial samples, whereas the dotted line to the uniaxial ones.

For a comparison with the commonly used materials, additional mechanical tests were conducted on PETG and PP prototype geogrids. The results pointed out two opposite behaviors, both for uniaxial and biaxial samples. As shown in Figure 9, TS values were $5.03 \pm 0.46$ kN/m and $4.89 \pm 0.46$ kN/m respectively for uniaxial and biaxial geogrids, whereas the elongation at break never exceeded 3% in all cases. Such results are very similar in both the prototype configurations. On the other hand, PP geogrids were characterized by a lower TS at yield, $1.04 \pm 0.08$ kN/m, and by a long elastic deformation phase followed by a likewise plastic deformation phase (Figure 10) with an elongation at break of 15–20% for the uniaxial model and 30–40% for the biaxial.

Finally, the mechanical tests conducted on the plastic-based materials allowed to compare the results and to discuss the intrinsic properties of biomaterials. PLA-natural fibers models were, on average, 35% less resistant to tension when compared with n-PLA ones; so, apparently, the geogrids geometry reduced the gap among the TS values of the biomaterials measured on the filaments. The ht-PLA made geogrids were the most tensile resistant and the only ones that presented TS values greater than n-PLA. Although the encouraging observations, all the PLA-based geogrid prototypes are very stiff. In fact, despite PP prototypes showed very low resistance to tension stress, they ensure a significant elasticity that, in some cases, must be requested for several geoengineering applications.

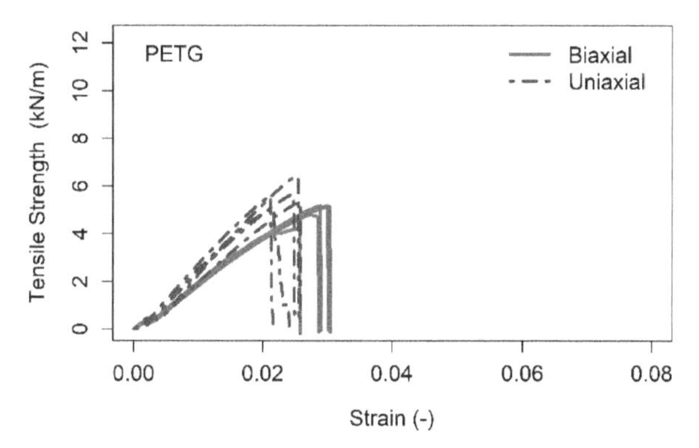


**Figure 9.** Stress-strain curves of PETG prototype geogrids: the continuous line corresponds to the biaxial samples, whereas the dotted line to the uniaxial ones.

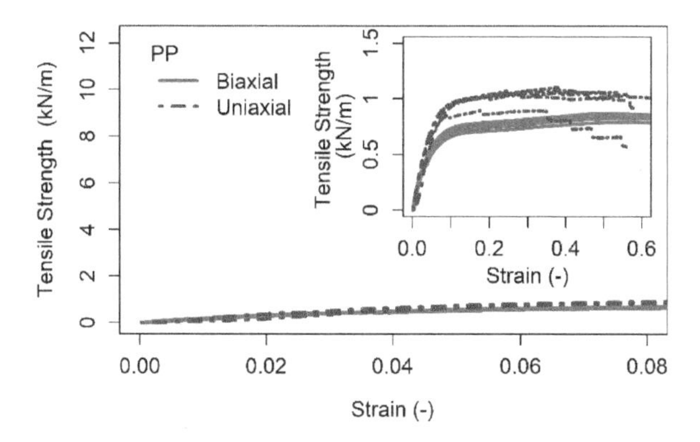


**Figure 10.** Stress-strain curves of PP prototype geogrids. In the inside panels, the stress-strain curves are zoomed to distinguish their characteristics. The continuous line corresponds to the biaxial samples, whereas the dotted line to the uniaxial ones.

## 4. Discussion

### *4.1. An Overview of Biomaterials: From the Mechanical Properties to the Biodegradation*

Many authors have already demonstrated through observations and measurements how the PLA-based biopolymer provides better performance in terms of mechanical resistance than other plastic-derived materials as PP [25]. In the present study, the measurements confirmed that PLA-based materials, in the most of cases, are more resistant under tensile stress than PP and PETG. In addition, it is significant how PP showed the lowest TS. Conversely, as expected, PLA and its blends showed to be very brittle with a scarce elongation at break. All tested materials exhibited an average elongation rate at break approximately to 2%, 600 times smaller than PP. This evidence causes some restrictions in its application and especially in civil engineering where the materials have to guarantee plastic deformation under high stress [16].

Concerning the integration of natural fibers, a discrepancy is evident between additive-enriched PLA filaments (ad-PLA and ht-PLA) and PLA-natural fibers blends (h-PLA, c-PLA and w-PLA). The natural fibers that integrated the neat-PLA matrix showed a maximum TS (23–28 MPa) lower than the n-PLA, partially offset by an increase of elasticity (approximately 3 GPa of YM) [77]. Thus, the present study did not assure that integrating PLA matrix with natural fibers provides noticeable advantages in terms of physical and mechanical properties respect than the neat material.

This range of values agree with other experiences conducted on PLA-based materials (Table 2) and includes the effects due to several factors such as the technology of 3D printer, the production process, the constituent structure, and contents. In particular, the different fabrication processes (fused deposition modeling, powder bed fusion, inject printing, stereolithography, direct energy deposition, laminated object manufacturing) are of relevant importance [78–80]. Among this variety of methods, however, the fused filament fabrication, the most used in the maker community and adopted in the present study, offers many advantages among which a relatively low melting point and a low request of energy [81]. Nevertheless, 3D process can induce an excessive porosity and crystallization among the layers, affecting the quality of the final product. To reduce the defects and improve the mechanical properties, a heat treatment post-3D printing could be an effective solution [82].

Another element of discussion is the degradability of PLA-based materials. The degradation of PLA can occur through abiotic process by the hydrolysis and/or biotic process by bacterial, fungal, and enzymatic activities. PLA clearly shows its eco-compatible characteristics decomposing into water, carbon dioxide and humus [15,17,83]. Despite its eco-friendly nature, PLA is moderately resistant to degradation processes, although can be influenced by several factors, including PLA own properties, as molecular weight and crystallinity, and environmental factors, such as humidity, temperature, pH and UV light [26]. For civil engineering applications, it is important to verify the biodegradation into the soil. On this topic, several studies carrying out soil burial tests investigated the decomposition of PLA under different shapes and its composites [64,84]. Generally, 1-year burial leads to minimal degradation under natural conditions (25 °C) [85–87]. Generally, PLA degradation in soil is slower than in compost medium because the latter usually has a higher moisture content and temperature range, enhancing PLA hydrolysis and assimilation by thermophilic microorganisms [88]. In addition, Calmon et al. (1999) [89] monitored the biodegradability of PLA films over 20 months showing minimal degradation or finding clear signs only after 2 years.

### *4.2. Applications in Geo-Environmental Engineering*

In the field of geo-environmental applications, the present study encourages the application of PLA-based materials to replace the most widely used petroleum-based materials as geosynthetics. They could be an excellent solution where it is required to perform a particular function for a limited time. A set of common applications can be: (i) *containment*, where it is important to limit the soil or sediment losses of a specific geometry; (ii) *protection layers*, where localized stresses cause damages to the soil surface; (iii) *soil reinforcement*, where the application consists of increasing the soil resistance to the sediment mobilization; (iv) *erosion control*, where surface erosion of soil particles is commonly due to surface water runoff and/or wind forces; and (v) *frictional interlayer*, where it is necessary to increase the friction at the interface between two different soil layers. Moreover, besides the optimum compatibility with the use in semi-natural and natural environment, PLA-based materials can promote the plant growth, especially the root system, through their degradation [90]. It is precisely such combination that could be the basis for designing a wide variety of soil-bioengineering measures. Among them, the geosynthetics reinforcing soil structures with vegetated face steep slopes remain the most common solution promoted by landscape engineers for the erosion control and the stabilization of the shallower soil layer [91,92]. To establish a permanent vegetation cover, seeding and live planting are the widely used method [93]. Seeding or hydro-seeding is traditionally recommended for a rapid slope-land revegetation [94], whereas the live planting that consists of installing unrooted cuttings vertically or perpendicularly to the slopes, is more expensive. Plant roots growing into the geogrids apertures can help to stabilize the soil shallower layer binding soil particles, increasing soil aggregation and anchoring the crossed soil mass to the fractures into the bedrock [93,95–99]. In addition, the vegetation cover minimizes the kinetic energy of raindrops, reduces runoff, and especially contrasts the soil erosion [100–104]. The vegetation contribution increases with increasing plant growth (and root system growth) and can compensate the degradation of the mechanical performance of PLA-based geogrids over the time. According to this proposal, adopting the PLA-based materials in the geo-environmental engineering practice allows the pursuit of the geotechnical objective (i.e., soil stabilization, erosion control) and the ecological-environmental purposes.

## 5. Conclusions

In the present study, laboratory tests were conducted on some biodegradable biopolymer based on PLA to characterize their properties in view of their use for geosynthetics production, as an alternative to petroleum-based polymers. An investigation on the global market of the bioplastics revealed how the PLA-based materials are the most promising for a wide range of applications in different fields (e.g., packaging, automotive products, consumer handled items, medical devices, etc.). Among a wide variety of biodegradable materials available on the market, 6 different PLA-based materials and 2 petroleum-derivatives were selected as the best candidate for the applications in geo-environmental engineering practice. Chemical and mechanical tests carried out on filaments (adapt for the 3D printing) showed a tensile resistance ranging from 23 to 52 MPa and an elastic modulus from 2.0 to 3.7 GPa with the presence of L-lactic acid that varies from 23.5 to 82.0%.

Furthermore, the production of uniaxial and biaxial small-scaled standard geogrids through a 3D printer allowed a robust comparison among them and among other materials as PETG and PP. As expected, the uniaxial geogrids were approximately 90% more resistant than the biaxial ones, considering all the tested cases. Among PLA-based, n-PLA and ht-PLA (i.e., with titanium dioxide) showed the best performance in terms of TS, 6.76 kN/m and 10.14 kN/m, respectively. Such values are approximately two times higher than the same prototype samples produced by PETG and are much higher than those guaranteed by PP geogrids. Despite the higher TS, PLA-based prototype samples were less elastic than those produced by PP that present an elongation at break up to 25%.

Finally, the biodegradable PLA or PLA-based polymers could be reliable and robust materials for the use in the field of geo-environmental (civil, geotechnical and soil-bio) engineering. Further investigations on their mechanical degradation under different field conditions (water, soil, rooted-soil, etc.) to verify their durability, will allow the establishment of whether these materials may actually represent an alternative to the petroleum-based products that cause serious impacts on the environment. Clearly, there is still a gap in terms of tensile strength between biopolymer-made and petroleum-based geosynthetics, but their use in combination with live plants, where the root system development initially supports and then gradually substitutes the biodegradable products in soil reinforcement, represents a promising research field.

**Author Contributions:** Conceptualization, A.C., P.S., C.G., and G.B.B.; methodology, A.C., P.S., and G.B.; software, A.C. and P.S.; validation, A.C., P.S. and G.B.; formal analysis, A.C., P.S. and G.B.; investigation, A.C., P.S. and G.B.B.; resources, C.G. and G.B.B.; data curation, A.C., P.S. and G.B.; writing—original draft preparation, A.C. and P.S.; writing—review and editing, A.C., P.S., G.B., C.G., and G.B.B; visualization, A.C. and P.S.; supervision, C.G. and G.B.B.; project administration, C.G. and G.B.B.; funding acquisition, C.G. and G.B.B. All authors have read and agreed to the published version of the manuscript.

**Funding:** This research was an integral part of the project TREE:HERO, acronym of "TREE distribution patterns: HillslopE failuRe prevention through forest management", entirely funded by Fondazione Cariplo (Italy; Ref. 2017–0714) in the framework of "Research dedicated to hydrogeological instability: a contribution to the prevision, prevention and risk mitigation".

**Acknowledgments:** The authors thank the Special Issue Editor Slobodan Mickovski and the two anonymous reviewers for their suggestions and comments.

**Conflicts of Interest:** The authors declare no conflict of interest.

## References


1. European Commission. *COM(2014) 398 Final;* Towards a Circular Economy: A ZeroWaste Programme for Europe; European Commission: Brussels, Belgium, 2014; p. 14.
2. Huang, B.; Wang, X.; Kua, H.; Geng, Y.; Bleischwitz, R.; Ren, J. Construction and Demolition Waste Management in China through the 3R Principle. *Resour. Conserv. Recycl.* **2018**, *129*, 36–44. [CrossRef]
3. Lu, W.; Yuan, H. A Framework for Understanding Waste Management Studies in Construction. *Waste Manag.* **2011**, *31*, 1252–1260. [CrossRef]
4. European Commission. *COM(2018) 35 Final;* On the Impact of the Use of Oxo-Degradable Plastic, Including Oxo-Degradable Plastic Carrier Bags, On the Environment; European Commission: Brussels, Belgium, 2018; p. 9.
5. Wiewel, B.V.; Lamoree, M. Geotextile Composition, Application and Ecotoxicology: A Review. *J. Hazard. Mater.* **2016**, *317*, 640–655. [CrossRef] [PubMed]
6. Müller, W.W.; Saathoff, F. Geosynthetics in Geoenvironmental Engineering. *Sci. Technol. Adv. Mater.* **2015**, *16*, 034605. [CrossRef]
7. Browne, M.A.; Galloway, T.; Thompson, R. Microplastic-an Emerging Contaminant of Potential Concern?: Learned Discourses. *Integr. Environ. Assess. Manag.* **2007**, *3*, 559–561. [CrossRef]
8. Beißmann, S.; Stiftinger, M.; Grabmayer, K.; Wallner, G.; Nitsche, D.; Buchberger, W. Monitoring the Degradation of Stabilization Systems in Polypropylene during Accelerated Aging Tests by Liquid Chromatography Combined with Atmospheric Pressure Chemical Ionization Mass Spectrometry. *Polym. Degrad. Stab.* **2013**, *98*, 1655–1661. [CrossRef]
9. Avella, M.; Buzarovska, A.; Errico, M.; Gentile, G.; Grozdanov, A. Eco-Challenges of Bio-Based Polymer Composites. *Materials* **2009**, *2*, 911–925. [CrossRef]
10. Pozo Morales, A.; Güemes, A.; Fernandez-Lopez, A.; Carcelen Valero, V.; De La Rosa Llano, S. Bamboo–Polylactic Acid (PLA) Composite Material for Structural Applications. *Materials* **2017**, *10*, 1286. [CrossRef] [PubMed]
11. Farah, S.; Anderson, D.G.; Langer, R. Physical and Mechanical Properties of PLA, and Their Functions in Widespread Applications: A Comprehensive Review. *Adv. Drug Deliv. Rev.* **2016**, *107*, 367–392. [CrossRef] [PubMed]
12. Gowthaman, S.; Nakashima, K.; Kawasaki, S. A State-of-the-Art Review on Soil Reinforcement Technology Using Natural Plant Fiber Materials: Past Findings, Present Trends and Future Directions. *Materials* **2018**, *11*, 553. [CrossRef] [PubMed]
13. Garlotta, D. A Literature Review of Poly(Lactic Acid). *J. Polym. Environ.* **2001**, *9*, 63–84. [CrossRef]
14. Jamshidian, M.; Tehrany, E.A.; Imran, M.; Jacquot, M.; Desobry, S. Poly-Lactic Acid: Production, Applications, Nanocomposites, and Release Studies. *Compr. Rev. Food Sci. Food Saf.* **2010**, *9*, 552–571. [CrossRef] [PubMed]
15. Tuominen, J.; Kylmä, J.; Kapanen, A.; Venelampi, O.; Itävaara, M.; Seppälä, J. Biodegradation of Lactic Acid Based Polymers under Controlled Composting Conditions and Evaluation of the Ecotoxicological Impact. *Biomacromolecules* **2002**, *3*, 445–455. [CrossRef]
16. Rasal, R.M.; Janorkar, A.V.; Hirt, D.E. Poly(Lactic Acid) Modifications. *Prog. Polym. Sci.* **2010**, *35*, 338–356. [CrossRef]
17. Drumright, R.E.; Gruber, P.R.; Henton, D.E. Polylactic Acid Technology. *Adv. Mater.* **2000**, *12*, 1841–1846. [CrossRef]
18. Farrington, D.W.; Davies, J.L.S.; Blackburn, R.S. Poly(lactic acid) fibers. In *Biodegradable and Sustainable Fibres;* Elsevier: Amsterdam, The Netherlands, 2005; pp. 191–220. ISBN 978-1-85573-916-1.
19. Pickering, K.L.; Aruan Efendy, M.G.; Le, T.M. A Review of Recent Developments in Natural Fibre Composites and Their Mechanical Performance. *Compos. Part A Appl. Sci. Manuf.* **2016**, *83*, 98–112. [CrossRef]
20. Faruk, O.; Bledzki, A.K.; Fink, H.-P.; Sain, M. Biocomposites Reinforced with Natural Fibers: 2000–2010. *Prog. Polym. Sci.* **2012**, *37*, 1552–1596. [CrossRef]
21. Ho, M.; Lau, K.; Wang, H.; Bhattacharyya, D. Characteristics of a Silk Fibre Reinforced Biodegradable Plastic. *Compos. Part B Eng.* **2011**, *42*, 117–122. [CrossRef]
22. Uddin, N.; Kalyankar, R.R. Manufacturing and Structural Feasibility of Natural Fiber Reinforced Polymeric Structural Insulated Panels for Panelized Construction. *Int. J. Polym. Sci.* **2011**, *2011*, 1–7. [CrossRef]
23. Bhatraju, N.S.; Kumar, K.K. To Learn on Construction of Pavement by Using Geotextile. *Int. J. Innov. Technol. Res.* **2018**, *6*, 7867–7869.
24. Jeon, H.-Y. Environmental Adaptability of Green Geosynthetics as Sustainable Materials for Civil Engineering Applications. In *Proceedings of the Geosynthetics, Forging a Path to Bona Fide Engineering Materials;* American Society of Civil Engineers: Chicago, IL, USA, 2016; pp. 318–325.
25. Murariu, M.; Dubois, P. PLA Composites: From Production to Properties. *Adv. Drug Deliv. Rev.* **2016**, *107*, 17–46. [CrossRef] [PubMed]
26. Karamanlioglu, M.; Preziosi, R.; Robson, G.D. Abiotic and Biotic Environmental Degradation of the Bioplastic Polymer Poly(Lactic Acid): A Review. *Polym. Degrad. Stab.* **2017**, *137*, 122–130. [CrossRef]
27. Lasprilla, A.J.R.; Martinez, G.A.R.; Lunelli, B.H.; Jardini, A.L.; Filho, R.M. Poly-Lactic Acid Synthesis for Application in Biomedical Devices: A Review. *Biotechnol. Adv.* **2012**, *30*, 321–328. [CrossRef] [PubMed]
28. Gunti, R.; Ratna Prasad, A.V.; Gupta, A.V.S.S.K.S. Mechanical and Degradation Properties of Natural Fiber-Reinforced PLA Composites: Jute, Sisal, and Elephant Grass. *Polym. Compos.* **2018**, *39*, 1125–1136. [CrossRef]
29. Mochane, M.J.; Mokhena, T.C.; Sadiku, E.R.; Ray, S.S.; Mofokeng, T.G. Green polymer composites based on polylactic acid (PLA) and fibers. In *Green Biopolymers and Their Nanocomposites;* Gnanasekaran, D., Ed.; Springer: Singapore, 2019; pp. 29–54. ISBN 9789811380624.

30. Ochi, S. Mechanical Properties of Kenaf Fibers and Kenaf/PLA Composites. *Mech. Mater.* **2008**, *40*, 446–452. [CrossRef]
31. Sun, Z.; Zhang, L.; Liang, D.; Xiao, W.; Lin, J. Mechanical and Thermal Properties of PLA Biocomposites Reinforced by Coir Fibers. *Int. J. Polym. Sci.* **2017**, *2017*, 1–8. [CrossRef]
32. Wang, Y.; Weng, Y.; Wang, L. Characterization of Interfacial Compatibility of Polylactic Acid and Bamboo Flour (PLA/BF) in Biocomposites. *Polym. Test.* **2014**, *36*, 119–125. [CrossRef]
33. Yu, T.; Ding, D.; Sheng, C.; Tuerhongjiang, T.; Li, Y. Enhanced Mechanical Properties and Flame Retardancy of Short Jute Fiber/Poly(Lactic Acid) Composites with Phosphorus-Based Compound. *Sci. China Technol. Sci.* **2017**, *60*, 1716–1723. [CrossRef]
34. Plackett, D.; Løgstrup Andersen, T.; Batsberg Pedersen, W.; Nielsen, L. Biodegradable Composites Based on L-Polylactide and Jute Fibres. *Compos. Sci. Technol.* **2003**, *63*, 1287–1296. [CrossRef]
35. Ben, G.; Kihara, Y. Development and Evaluation of Mechanical Properties for Kenaf Fibers/PLA Composites. *Key Eng. Mater.* **2007**, *334–335*, 489–492. [CrossRef]
36. Saenghirunwattana, P.; Noomhorm, A.; Rungsardthong, V. Mechanical Properties of Soy Protein Based "Green" Composites Reinforced with Surface Modified Cornhusk Fiber. *Ind. Crop. Prod.* **2014**, *60*, 144–150. [CrossRef]
37. Graupner, N.; Herrmann, A.S.; Müssig, J. Natural and Man-Made Cellulose Fibre-Reinforced Poly(Lactic Acid) (PLA) Composites: An Overview about Mechanical Characteristics and Application Areas. *Compos. Part A Appl. Sci. Manuf.* **2009**, *40*, 810–821. [CrossRef]
38. Bax, B.; Müssig, J. Impact and Tensile Properties of PLA/Cordenka and PLA/Flax Composites. *Compos. Sci. Technol.* **2008**, *68*, 1601–1607. [CrossRef]
39. Yu, T.; Ren, J.; Li, S.; Yuan, H.; Li, Y. Effect of Fiber Surface-Treatments on the Properties of Poly(Lactic Acid)/Ramie Composites. *Compos. Part A Appl. Sci. Manuf.* **2010**, *41*, 499–505. [CrossRef]
40. Febrianto, F.; Yoshioka, M.; Nagai, Y.; Syafii, W.; Shiraishi, N. Characterization and Properties of Composites of Wood Flour and Poly Lactic Acid. *Mokchae Konghak* **2006**, *34*, 67–78.
41. Muller, J.; González-Martínez, C.; Chiralt, A. Combination of Poly(Lactic) Acid and Starch for Biodegradable Food Packaging. *Materials* **2017**, *10*, 952. [CrossRef] [PubMed]
42. Finkenstadt, V.L.; Liu, C.-K.; Evangelista, R.; Liu, L.; Cermak, S.C.; Hojilla-Evangelista, M.; Willett, J.L. Poly(Lactic Acid) Green Composites Using Oilseed Coproducts as Fillers. *Ind. Crop. Prod.* **2007**, *26*, 36–43. [CrossRef]
43. Rawi, N.F.M.; Jayaraman, K.; Bhattacharyya, D. A Performance Study on Composites Made from Bamboo Fabric and Poly(Lactic Acid). *J. Reinf. Plast. Compos.* **2013**, *32*, 1513–1525. [CrossRef]
44. Hu, R.; Lim, J.-K. Fabrication and Mechanical Properties of Completely Biodegradable Hemp Fiber Reinforced Polylactic Acid Composites. *J. Compos. Mater.* **2007**, *41*, 1655–1669. [CrossRef]
45. Ma, H.; Joo, C.W. Structure and Mechanical Properties of Jute-Polylactic Acid Biodegradable Composites. *J. Compos. Mater.* **2011**, *45*, 1451–1460. [CrossRef]
46. Bledzki, A.K.; Jaszkiewicz, A.; Scherzer, D. Mechanical Properties of PLA Composites with Man-Made Cellulose and Abaca Fibres. *Compos. Part A Appl. Sci. Manuf.* **2009**, *40*, 404–412. [CrossRef]
47. Oksman, K.; Skrifvars, M.; Selin, J.-F. Natural Fibres as Reinforcement in Polylactic Acid (PLA) Composites. *Compos. Sci. Technol.* **2003**, *63*, 1317–1324. [CrossRef]
48. Jandas, P.J.; Mohanty, A.K.; Nayak, S.K.; Srivastava, H. Effect of Surface Treatments of Banana Fiber on Mechanical, Thermal, and Biodegradability Properties of PLA/Banana Fiber Biocomposites. *Polym Compos* **2011**, *32*, 1689–1700. [CrossRef]
49. Shih, Y.-F.; Huang, C.-C. Polylactic Acid (PLA)/Banana Fiber (BF) Biodegradable Green Composites. *J. Polym. Res.* **2011**, *18*, 2335–2340. [CrossRef]
50. Song, Y.S.; Lee, J.T.; Ji, D.S.; Kim, M.W.; Lee, S.H.; Youn, J.R. Viscoelastic and Thermal Behavior of Woven Hemp Fiber Reinforced Poly(Lactic Acid) Composites. *Compos. Part B Eng.* **2012**, *43*, 856–860. [CrossRef]
51. Porras, A.; Maranon, A. Development and Characterization of a Laminate Composite Material from Polylactic Acid (PLA) and Woven Bamboo Fabric. *Compos. Part B Eng.* **2012**, *43*, 2782–2788. [CrossRef]
52. Ibrahim, N.A.; Yunus, W.M.Z.W.; Othman, M.; Abdan, K.; Hadithon, K.A. Poly(Lactic Acid) (PLA)-Reinforced Kenaf Bast Fiber Composites: The Effect of Triacetin. *J. Reinf. Plast. Compos.* **2010**, *29*, 1099–1111. [CrossRef]
53. Lee, S.-H.; Wang, S. Biodegradable Polymers/Bamboo Fiber Biocomposite with Bio-Based Coupling Agent. *Compos. Part A: Appl. Sci. Manuf.* **2006**, *37*, 80–91. [CrossRef]
54. Ruksakulpiwat, Y.; Tonimit, P.; Kluengsamrong, J. Mechanical Properties of PLA-Jute Composites by Using Natural Rubber and Epoxidized Natural Rubber as Impact Modifiers: Effect of Molding Technique. *Clean Technol.* **2010**, *4*, 310–313.
55. Taha, I.; Ziegmann, G. A Comparison of Mechanical Properties of Natural Fiber Filled Biodegradable and Polyolefin Polymers. *J. Compos. Mater.* **2006**, *40*, 1933–1946. [CrossRef]
56. Stoof, D.; Pickering, K.; Zhang, Y. Fused Deposition Modelling of Natural Fibre/Polylactic Acid Composites. *J. Compos. Sci.* **2017**, *1*, 8. [CrossRef]
57. Le Duigou, A.; Pillin, I.; Bourmaud, A.; Davies, P.; Baley, C. Effect of Recycling on Mechanical Behaviour of Biocompostable Flax/Poly(l-Lactide) Composites. *Compos. Part A Appl. Sci. Manuf.* **2008**, *39*, 1471–1478. [CrossRef]
58. Yu, T.; Li, Y.; Ren, J. Preparation and Properties of Short Natural Fiber Reinforced Poly(Lactic Acid) Composites. *Trans. Nonferrous Met. Soc. China* **2009**, *19*, s651–s655. [CrossRef]

59. Kuciel, S.; Mazur, K.; Hebda, M. The Influence of Wood and Basalt Fibres on Mechanical, Thermal and Hydrothermal Properties of PLA Composites. *J Polym Environ.* **2020**, *28*, 1204–1215. [CrossRef]
60. Mazzanti, V.; Pariante, R.; Bonanno, A.; Ruiz de Ballesteros, O.; Mollica, F.; Filippone, G. Reinforcing Mechanisms of Natural Fibers in Green Composites: Role of Fibers Morphology in a PLA/Hemp Model System. *Compos. Sci. Technol.* **2019**, *180*, 51–59. [CrossRef]
61. Suryanegara, L.; Nakagaito, A.N.; Yano, H. The Effect of Crystallization of PLA on the Thermal and Mechanical Properties of Microfibrillated Cellulose-Reinforced PLA Composites. *Compos. Sci. Technol.* **2009**, *69*, 1187–1192. [CrossRef]
62. Graupner, N.; Narkpiban, K.; Poonsawat, T.; Tooptompong, P.; Müssig, J. Toddy Palm (Borassus Flabellifer) Fruit Fibre Bundles as Reinforcement in Polylactide (PLA) Composites: An Overview about Fibre and Composite Characteristics. *J. Renew. Mater.* **2019**, *7*, 693–711. [CrossRef]
63. Duan, J.; Wu, H.; Fu, W.; Hao, M. Mechanical Properties of Hybrid Sisal/Coir Fibers Reinforced Polylactide Biocomposites. *Polym. Compos.* **2018**, *39*, E188–E199. [CrossRef]
64. Dong, Y.; Ghataura, A.; Takagi, H.; Haroosh, H.J.; Nakagaito, A.N.; Lau, K.-T. Polylactic Acid (PLA) Biocomposites Reinforced with Coir Fibres: Evaluation of Mechanical Performance and Multifunctional Properties. *Compos. Part A Appl. Sci. Manuf.* **2014**, *63*, 76–84. [CrossRef]
65. Marques, D.S.; Gil, M.H.; Baptista, C.M.S.G. Bulk Polytransesterification of L-Lactic Acid Esters: An Alternative Route to Synthesize Poly(Lactic Acid). *J. Appl. Polym. Sci.* **2012**, *125*, E283–E289. [CrossRef]
66. Hufenus, R.; Rueegger, R.; Banjac, R.; Mayor, P.; Springman, S.M.; Bronnimann, R. Full-Scale Field Tests on Geosynthetic Reinforced Unpaved Roads on Soft Subgrade. *Geotext. Geomembr.* **2006**, *24*, 21–37. [CrossRef]
67. Yoo, C.; Lee, D. Performance of Geogrid-Encased Stone Columns in Soft Ground: Full-Scale Load Tests. *Geosynth. Int.* **2012**, *19*, 480–490. [CrossRef]
68. Bathurst, R.J.; Vlachopoulos, N.; Walters, D.L.; Burgess, P.G.; Allen, T.M. The Influence of Facing Stiffness on the Performance of Two Geosynthetic Reinforced Soil Retaining Walls. *Can. Geotech. J.* **2006**, *43*, 1225–1237. [CrossRef]
69. Garnier, J.; Gaudin, C.; Springman, S.M.; Culligan, P.J.; Goodings, D.; Konig, D.; Kutter, B.; Phillips, R.; Randolph, M.F.; Thorel, L. Catalogue of Scaling Laws and Similitude Questions in Geotechnical Centrifuge Modelling. *Int. J. Phys. Model. Geotech.* **2007**, *7*, 01–23. [CrossRef]
70. Springman, S.M.; Bolton, M.D.; Sharma, J.; Balachandran, S. Modelling and instrumentation of a geotextile in the geotechnical centrifuge. In Proceedings of the International Symposyum on Earth Reinforcement Practice, Kyushu, Japan, 11–13 November 1992; 167, pp. 172–178.
71. Amurane, I.; Zhang, M.; Li, T.; Jiang, H. Optimization of 3D Printed Geocells Based on Numerical Simulation and Experimental Investigation. *IOP Conf. Ser. Earth Environ. Sci.* **2019**, *233*, 032043. [CrossRef]
72. Arab, M.G.; Omar, M.; Alotaibi, E.; Mostafa, O.; Naeem, M.; Badr, O. Bio-Inspired 3D-Printed Honeycomb for Soil Reinforcement. In *Proceedings of the Geo-Congress 2020*; American Society of Civil Engineers: Minneapolis, Minnesota, 2020; pp. 262–271.
73. Mallett, S.D.; Matsumura, S.; David Frost, J. Additive Manufacturing and Computed Tomography of Bio-Inspired Anchorage Systems. *Géotechnique Lett.* **2018**, *8*, 219–225. [CrossRef]
74. Stathas, D.; Wang, J.P.; Ling, H.I. Model Geogrids and 3D Printing. *Geotext. Geomembr.* **2017**, *45*, 688–696. [CrossRef]
75. Viswanadham, B.V.S.; Jessberger, H.L. Centrifuge Modeling of Geosynthetic Reinforced Clay Liners of Landfills. *J. Geotech. Geoenviron. Eng.* **2005**, *131*, 564–574. [CrossRef]
76. Viswanadham, B.V.S.; König, D. Studies on Scaling and Instrumentation of a Geogrid. *Geotext. Geomembr.* **2004**, *22*, 307–328. [CrossRef]
77. Cislaghi, A.; Sala, P.; Borgonovo, G.; Gandolfi, C.; Bischetti, G.B. Biodegradable geosynthetics for geotechnical and geo-environmental engineering. In *Innovative Biosystems Engineering for Sustainable Agriculture, Forestry and Food Production*; Coppola, A., Di Renzo, G.C., Altieri, G., D'Antonio, P., Eds.; Lecture Notes in Civil Engineering; Springer International Publishing: Cham, Switerland, 2020; Volume 67, pp. 49–57. ISBN 978-3-030-39298-7.
78. Ngo, T.D.; Kashani, A.; Imbalzano, G.; Nguyen, K.T.Q.; Hui, D. Additive Manufacturing (3D Printing): A Review of Materials, Methods, Applications and Challenges. *Compos. Part B Eng.* **2018**, *143*, 172–196. [CrossRef]
79. Bandyopadhyay, A.; Heer, B. Additive Manufacturing of Multi-Material Structures. *Mater. Sci. Eng. R Rep.* **2018**, *129*, 1–16. [CrossRef]
80. Bose, S.; Ke, D.; Sahasrabudhe, H.; Bandyopadhyay, A. Additive Manufacturing of Biomaterials. *Prog. Mater. Sci.* **2018**, *93*, 45–111. [CrossRef] [PubMed]
81. Brenken, B.; Barocio, E.; Favaloro, A.; Kunc, V.; Pipes, R.B. Fused Filament Fabrication of Fiber-Reinforced Polymers: A Review. *Addit. Manuf.* **2018**, *21*, 1–16. [CrossRef]
82. Liao, Y.; Liu, C.; Coppola, B.; Barra, G.; Di Maio, L.; Incarnato, L.; Lafdi, K. Effect of Porosity and Crystallinity on 3D Printed PLA Properties. *Polymers* **2019**, *11*, 1487. [CrossRef]
83. Ghorpade, V.M.; Gennadios, A.; Hanna, M.A. Laboratory Composting of Extruded Poly(Lactic Acid) Sheets q. *Bioresour. Technol.* **2001**, *76*, 57–61. [CrossRef]
84. Weng, Y.-X.; Jin, Y.-J.; Meng, Q.-Y.; Wang, L.; Zhang, M.; Wang, Y.-Z. Biodegradation Behavior of Poly(Butylene Adipate-Co-Terephthalate) (PBAT), Poly(Lactic Acid) (PLA), and Their Blend under Soil Conditions. *Polym. Test.* **2013**, *32*, 918–926. [CrossRef]

85. Karamanlioglu, M.; Houlden, A.; Robson, G.D. Isolation and Characterisation of Fungal Communities Associated with Degradation and Growth on the Surface of Poly(Lactic) Acid (PLA) in Soil and Compost. *Int. Biodeterior. Biodegrad.* **2014**, *95*, 301–310. [CrossRef]
86. Rudnik, E.; Briassoulis, D. Degradation Behaviour of Poly(Lactic Acid) Films and Fibres in Soil under Mediterranean Field Conditions and Laboratory Simulations Testing. *Ind. Crop. Prod.* **2011**, *33*, 648–658. [CrossRef]
87. Shogren, R.L.; Doane, W.M.; Garlotta, D.; Lawton, J.W.; Willett, J.L. Biodegradation of Starch/Polylactic Acid/Poly(Hydroxyester-Ether) Composite Bars in Soil. *Polym. Degrad. Stab.* **2003**, *79*, 405–411. [CrossRef]
88. Itävaara, M.; Karjomaa, S.; Selin, J.-F. Biodegradation of Polylactide in Aerobic and Anaerobic Thermophilic Conditions. *Chemosphere* **2002**, *46*, 879–885. [CrossRef]
89. Calmon, A.; Guillaume, S.; Bellon-Maurel, V.; Feuilloley, P.; Silvestre, F. Evaluation of Material Biodegradability in Real Conditions-Development of a Burial Test and an Analysis Methodology Based on Numerical Vision. *J. Environ. Polym. Degrad.* **1999**, *7*, 157–166. [CrossRef]
90. Kinnersley, A.M.; Scott, T.C.; Yopp, J.H.; Whitten, G.H. Promotion of Plant Growth by Polymers of Lactic Acid. *Plant Growth Regul.* **1990**, *9*, 137–146. [CrossRef]
91. Bischetti, G.B.; Di Fidio, M.; Florineth, F. On the Origin of Soil Bioengineering. *Landsc. Res.* **2014**, *39*, 583–595. [CrossRef]
92. Cazzuffi, D.; Cardile, G.; Gioffrè, D. Geosynthetic Engineering and Vegetation Growth in Soil Reinforcement Applications. *Transp. Infrastruct. Geotechnol.* **2014**, *1*, 262–300. [CrossRef]
93. Gray, D.H.; Sotir, R.B. *Biotechnical and Soil Bioengineering Slope Stabilization: A Practical Guide for Erosion Control*; John Wiley & Sons: Hoboken, NJ, USA, 1996; ISBN 978-0-471-04978-4.
94. Fox, J.L.; Bhattarai, S.P.; Gyasi-Agyei, Y. Evaluation of Different Seed Mixtures for Grass Establishment to Mitigate Soil Erosion on Steep Slopes of Railway Batters. *J. Irrig. Drain Eng.* **2011**, *137*, 624–631. [CrossRef]
95. Bischetti, G.B.; Chiaradia, E.A.; D'Agostino, V.; Simonato, T. Quantifying the Effect of Brush Layering on Slope Stability. *Ecol. Eng.* **2010**, *36*, 258–264. [CrossRef]
96. Cislaghi, A.; Giupponi, L.; Tamburini, A.; Giorgi, A.; Bischetti, G.B. The Effects of Mountain Grazing Abandonment on Plant Community, Forage Value and Soil Properties: Observations and Field Measurements in an Alpine Area. *CATENA* **2019**, *181*, 104086. [CrossRef]
97. De Baets, S.; Poesen, J.; Gyssels, G.; Knapen, A. Effects of Grass Roots on the Erodibility of Topsoils during Concentrated Flow. *Geomorphology* **2006**, *76*, 54–67. [CrossRef]
98. Gyssels, G.; Poesen, J.; Bochet, E.; Li, Y. Impact of Plant Roots on the Resistance of Soils to Erosion by Water: A Review. *Prog. Phys. Geogr.* **2005**, *29*, 189–217. [CrossRef]
99. Lian, B.; Peng, J.; Zhan, H.; Wang, X. Mechanical Response of Root-Reinforced Loess with Various Water Contents. *Soil Tillage Res.* **2019**, *193*, 85–94. [CrossRef]
100. Bastola, S.; Ishidaira, H.; Takeuchi, K. Regionalisation of Hydrological Model Parameters under Parameter Uncertainty: A Case Study Involving TOPMODEL and Basins across the Globe. *J. Hydrol.* **2008**, *357*, 188–206. [CrossRef]
101. Gray, D.H.; Leiser, A.T. *Biotechnical Slope Protection and Erosion Control*; Van Nostrand Reinhold Company Inc.: New York, NY, USA, 1982; ISBN 0-442-21222-4.
102. Zhang, X.; Zhao, W.; Wang, L.; Liu, Y.; Feng, Q.; Fang, X.; Liu, Y. Distribution of Shrubland and Grassland Soil Erodibility on the Loess Plateau. *Int. J. Environ. Res. Public Health* **2018**, *15*, 1193. [CrossRef]
103. Gonzalez-Ollauri, A.; Mickovski, S.B. Plant-Best: A Novel Plant Selection Tool for Slope Protection. *Ecol. Eng.* **2017**, *106*, 154–173. [CrossRef]
104. Gonzalez-Ollauri, A.; Mickovski, S.B. Using the Root Spread Information of Pioneer Plants to Quantify Their Mitigation Potential against Shallow Landslides and Erosion in Temperate Humid Climates. *Ecol. Eng.* **2016**, *95*, 302–315. [CrossRef]

*Article*

# Experimental and Numerical Analysis for Earth-Fill Dam Seepage

**Ahmed Mohammed Sami Al-Janabi [1], Abdul Halim Ghazali [1], Yousry Mahmoud Ghazaw [2,3], Haitham Abdulmohsin Afan [4], Nadhir Al-Ansari [5] and Zaher Mundher Yaseen [6,*]**

1 Department of Civil Engineering, Faculty of Engineering, Universiti Putra Malaysia, UPM Serdang, Selangor 43400, Malaysia; huffad@yahoo.com (A.M.S.A.-J.); abdhalim@upm.edu.my (A.H.G.)
2 Department of Irrigation and Hydraulics, Faculty of Engineering, Alexandria University, Alexandria 21544, Egypt; ghazaw@qec.edu.sa
3 Department of Civil Engineering, College of Engineering, Qassim University, Buraydah 51431, Saudi Arabia
4 Institute of Research and Development, Duy Tan University, Da Nang 550000, Vietnam; haithamabdulmohsinafan@duytan.edu.vn
5 Civil, Environmental and Natural Resources Engineering, Lulea University of Technology, 97187 Lulea, Sweden; nadhir.alansari@ltu.se
6 Sustainable Developments in Civil Engineering Research Group, Faculty of Civil Engineering, Ton Duc Thang University, Ho Chi Minh City, Vietnam
* Correspondence: yaseen@tdtu.edu.vn

Received: 25 February 2020; Accepted: 20 March 2020; Published: 22 March 2020

**Abstract:** Earth-fill dams are the most common types of dam and the most economical choice. However, they are more vulnerable to internal erosion and piping due to seepage problems that are the main causes of dam failure. In this study, the seepage through earth-fill dams was investigated using physical, mathematical, and numerical models. Results from the three methods revealed that both mathematical calculations using L. Casagrande solutions and the SEEP/W numerical model have a plotted seepage line compatible with the observed seepage line in the physical model. However, when the seepage flow intersected the downstream slope and when piping took place, the use of SEEP/W to calculate the flow rate became useless as it was unable to calculate the volume of water flow in pipes. This was revealed by the big difference in results between physical and numerical models in the first physical model, while the results were compatible in the second physical model when the seepage line stayed within the body of the dam and low compacted soil was adopted. Seepage analysis for seven different configurations of an earth-fill dam was conducted using the SEEP/W model at normal and maximum water levels to find the most appropriate configuration among them. The seven dam configurations consisted of four homogenous dams and three zoned dams. Seepage analysis revealed that if sufficient quantity of silty sand soil is available around the proposed dam location, a homogenous earth-fill dam with a medium drain length of 0.5 m thickness is the best design configuration. Otherwise, a zoned earth-fill dam with a central core and 1:0.5 Horizontal to Vertical ratio (H:V) is preferred.

**Keywords:** Seepage; Earth-fill dam; Experimental analysis; Numerical analysis; SEEP/W model; Dam safety and sustainability

## 1. Introduction

### 1.1. Research Background

Earth-fill (embankment) dams are the most common types of dam. In addition, they are considered as the most economical choice when utilizing locally available materials. Further, they have been part of a usual practice to store and control river water for a long time [1,2]. Such dams are normally built by placement and compaction of a complex semi-plastic mound of various soil, rock, sand, or clay compositions [3]. Stability and seepage are important in an earth dam as they were found to be the main reasons of dam failure [4,5]. Earth-fill dams lose water from the dam reservoir through evaporation and from the dam body through seepage [6–8]. Losses due to evaporation cannot be controlled, but with good construction techniques, seepage losses can be minimized [9]. Seepage is the outcome of the difference in water height upstream and downstream. Seepage rate depends on various factors, including the soil medium, the type of fluid, as well as the dams' geometric conditions [10–12].

Soil seepage, which is the hydraulic conductivity of the soil and the pressure gradient, can be affected by a combination of factors acting on water [13]. Seepage in both homogenous and non-homogeneous earth-fill dams occur from the slow percolation of water on the dam and its foundation [14]. Inadequate seepage control has led to several seepage-related problems and failures on earth-fill dams [15]. Earth dams are more susceptible to internal erosion and piping due to seepage and require continuous maintenance. As the internal erosion and piping due to seepage are the main causes of failure in earth-fill dams, the control of seepage is extremely important in the design, construction, and safe operation of dams [4,9,16]. Although all earth-fill dams have at least some seepage, designing such dams should takes sufficient control of seepage into consideration, in order to ensure that the seepage does not adversely affect the safety and sustainability of the dam.

Several theories including Dupuit's, Schaffernak–VanIterson's, and Casagrande's have been used to determine the seepage line and calculate the seepage rate through earth-fill dams [17–19]. In addition, several studies have been numerically and experimentally performed with the aim of calculating the seepage rate and the ways to minimize it [17,20–24]. This study aims to investigate the seepage line through earth-fill dams and estimate the rate of seepage using three methods, namely, physical models, mathematical calculations, and numerical models. This study also aims to investigate how the results from mathematical calculations and numerical models fit the observed seepage line and rate from the physical models.

### *1.2. Study of Seepage Through Earth-Fill Dams*

The dam failures recorded in the 1700s and 1800s motivated the research for more scientific ways of designing and constructing dams. The first studies that quantitatively represented fluid flow through a porous media were published by Henri Darcy in 1856; he based his formula (now popular as Darcy's law) on the flow of water through vertical filters in laboratory set-ups [25]. From the experiments, he demonstrated a simple relationship between the discharge velocity and the hydraulic gradient which he expressed as follows:

$$v_d = k \cdot i = Q/A \tag{1}$$

$$Q = k \cdot i \cdot A \tag{2}$$

where $Q$ is rate of seepage (m$^3$/s), $v_d$ is discharge velocity (m/s), $i$ is hydraulic gradient (m/m), $k$ is coefficient of permeability (m/s), and $A$ is cross-sectional area normal to the direction of flow (m$^2$).

In the 1880s, Forchheimer demonstrated that the distribution of water pressure and velocity within a seepage medium is governed by the Laplace differential equation. Early in the 1900s, a powerful graphical method was developed independently by Forchhiemer in Germany and Richardson in England to obtain approximate solutions of the Laplace equation [26]. This method was widely used for earth dams after the publication of a comprehensive research that was conducted by researchers [19]. Since then, the solution of the Laplace equation by the graphical procedure or with electrical analog models has become a standard procedure for seepage analysis [4]. However, the graphical method requires a long procedure of plotting, is time consuming, and subjected to personal skills [4]. The rate of seepage using the L. Casagrande solution (Figure 1) is:

$$q = k \cdot a \cdot sin^2 \beta \tag{3}$$

where $q$ is the Darcy flux or flow rate ($m^2/s$), $k$ is the hydraulic conductivity or permeability (m/s), $a$ is the length of the seepage surface (m), and $\beta$ is the angle of the downstream slope.

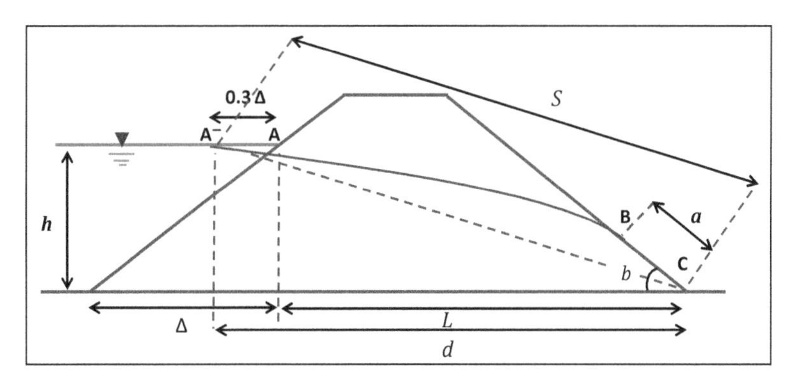


**Figure 1.** L. Casagrande's solution for flow through an earth dam [27].

The length of the seepage surface $a$ using upstream head $h$ is calculated as:

$$a = S - \sqrt{S^2 - \frac{h^2}{sin^2\beta}} \tag{4}$$

where $S$ is the length of the curve $\bar{A}$BC (m), and $h$ is the upstream head (m).

However, with about a 4–5% error, we can approximate $S$ as the length of the straight line $\bar{A}$C. Hence:

$$S = \sqrt{d^2 + h^2} \tag{5}$$

$$d = L + 0.3\Delta \tag{6}$$

### *1.3. The Use of Physical and Numerical Models*

Although the study of seepage through earth-fill dam needs an investigation of hydrological and geological conditions in sites, numerous studies have been conducted using physical models, (e.g., [16,28,29]), because physical models give a general picture of seepage behavior through earth-fill dams, including the phreatic line and the flow rate. Moreover, tests conducted on physical models can be an essential tool for investigating seepage behavior before the construction of the earth-fill dams and help to verify the initial design of dams by revealing potential demerits of a proposed design and to explore solutions.

However, as physical modeling has many limitations and constraints, the numerical modeling which is based on the mathematical solutions is the other way used in many researches (e.g., [30–32]), to solve the most complex engineering problems including seepage studies.

Numerical modeling is a rapid and less expensive technique and its results can be easily shared with the concerned parties. Being a purely mathematical approach, numerical modeling differs significantly from both laboratory-scale physical and full-scaled field modeling [10]. In situations where numerical modeling is considered improperly validated, physical modeling is normally recommended; such situations may include complex hydraulic conditions, non-standard or irregular site-specific conditions, or project performance improvement using non-standard designs.

In this study, the seepage through earth-fill dams was investigated using three methods, namely, physical, mathematical, and numerical models, and then the results were compared with each other. Subsequently, an example of seepage analysis for seven different configurations of an earth-fill dam was conducted using the SEEP/W software.

## 2. Materials and Methods

### 2.1. Experimental Setup

Two physical models of earth-fill dam were constructed in the hydraulic laboratory at Universiti Putra Malaysia. The models were placed inside rectangular tanks made of Perspex acrylic clear sheets, each with a length of 2.4 m, width of 0.5 m, and height of 0.5 m (Figure 2). Both models were homogenous with different drainage configuration, one with toe drain and the other with maximum length of horizontal drain.

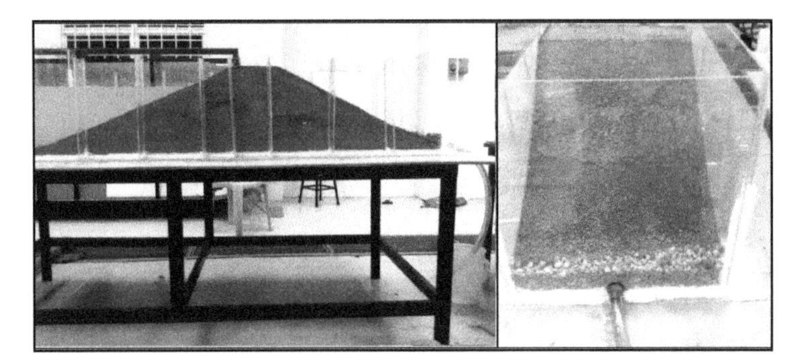

**Figure 2.** Earth-fill dam models inside the rectangular tanks.

The maximum length of horizontal drain was calculated using an equation [33] which is expressed as follows:

$$L_{\max} = F_b\,(m+n) + T + h\frac{1+n^2}{2n^2} \times [0.3m + n - \sqrt{(0.3m+n)^2 - n^2}] \quad (7)$$

where $L_{\max}$ is the length of horizontal drain (m), $F_b$ is free board (m), $m$ is upstream slope (m), $n$ is downstream slope (m), $T$ is crest width (m), and $h$ is upstream head (m).

Details of models' cross-sections are shown in Figure 3. Soil used to construct the earth-fill dam models was collected from the area of Gabai River near Langat Dam located in Hulu Langat, Selangor, Malaysia. Laboratory tests revealed that the soil sample was silty-sand, the optimum moisture of soil compaction was 20%, and the hydraulic conductivities for well and low compacted soil were $1.74562 \times 10^{-8}$ m/s and $3.493 \times 10^{-6}$ m/s, respectively. For the toe and horizontal drains, gravel with hydraulic conductivity of 0.016 m/s was used. During the construction of the physical models, soil was placed in layers of 5 cm and compacted accordingly, and the slopes of dam upstream and downstream were further compacted to fit the slope of 2.5:1 and 2:1 respectively.

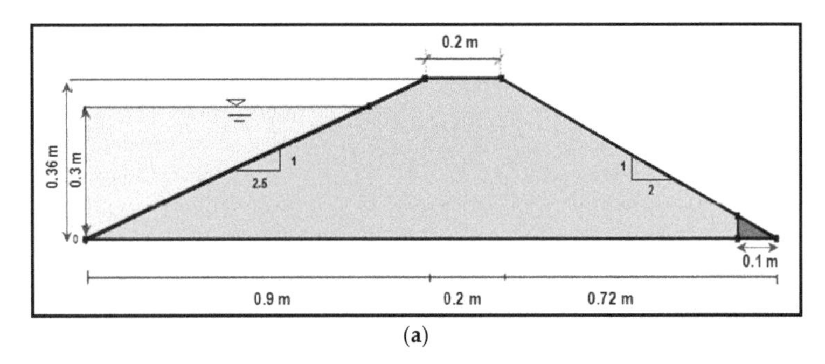


(a)

**Figure 3.** *Cont.*

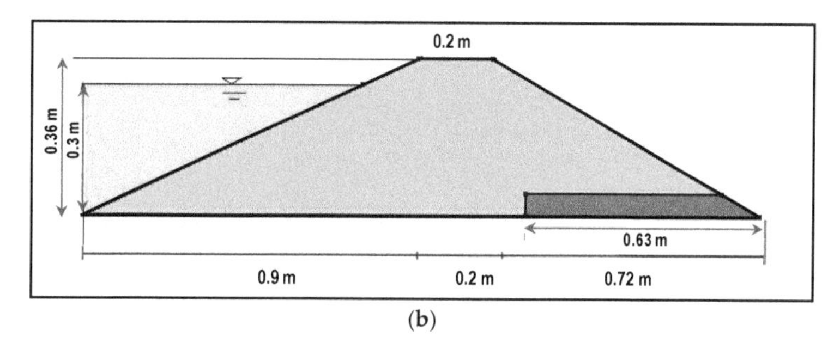


(b)

**Figure 3.** The cross-sections of the physical earth-fill dam models: (**a**) model with toe drain, (**b**) model with maximum drain length.

### 2.2. Experimental Tests

The experiments were carried out with a constant upstream water level of 0.3 m. The reservoir of dam models was filled in water to the target level and kept at that level up to 9 h to get a fully saturated soil that has a constant seepage rate. To observe the phreatic line, four holes were drilled in the downstream slope of the dam to measure the height of water. Heights of the holes from the heel of the dam models were 0.87, 1.04, 1.28, and 1.46 m. The seepage rate through the dam models was calculated by a volumetric method, which involves measuring the volume of water outflow from the model. Hence, the total seepage rate was calculated by dividing the volume of water collected from the outlet (Figure 2) in a certain period of time.

### 2.3. Mathematical Calculation Using L. Casagrande Solution

The mathematical and graphical methods proposed by some researchers [34] were used to plot the phreatic line through the two physical models of earth-fill dam. Five and four points were allocated along the x-axis of models with toe drain and with maximum length of horizontal drain, respectively. The rate of seepage has been calculated mathematically using the L. Casagrande mathematical solution (Equations (3)–(6)).

### 2.4. Numerical Modeling Using SEEP/W Software

The SEEP/W software is a numerical model that depends on the finite element method. It can mathematically simulate the real physical process of water flowing through a particulate medium. The program deals with the fundamental flow laws for steady state and transient flow, and it shows how these laws are represented in numerical form. The mathematical equations used in SEEP/W are Darcy's law, partial differential water flow equations, finite element water flow equations, temporal integration, numerical integration, hydraulic conductivity matrix, mass matrix, flux boundary vector, and density-dependent flow. In this study, the SEEP/W program was used to plot the phreatic line through the two physical models of earth-fill dam and to calculate the seepage rate through them.

## 3. Results and Analysis

### 3.1. Earth-Fill Dam Model with Toe Drain

For the dam model with toe drain, observations revealed that the heights of phreatic line were 0.27, 0.24, 0.193, and 0.175 m for holes located in 0.87, 1.04, 1.28, and 1.46 m from the heel of the dam models, respectively. Observations also revealed that some of the seepage exited at the downstream face of the dam model and flow out between the distances of 1.41 to 1.48 m from the heel of the dam (Figure 4). This phreatic line intersection with the downstream slope would influence the stability of the earth dam because of potential piping. The total seepage flow through the model was $6.3889 \times 10^{-7}$ $m^3/s$ (2.3 l/h), and the discharge of seepage was $1.277 \times 10^{-6}$ $m^3/s/m$.

**Figure 4.** Seepage line touches the downstream slope of the model with toe drain.

Mathematical calculations using L. Casagrande solutions showed that the seepage losses through the dam were $q = 6.4588 \times 10^{-10}$ and $1.2924 \times 10^{-7}$ m$^3$/s/m for well and low compacted soil, respectively, and the heights of phreatic line were 0.267, 0.243, 0.203 0.167, and 0.037 m for points located 0.82, 0.99, 1.23, 1.41, and 1.77 m from the heel of the dam, respectively (Figure 5a).

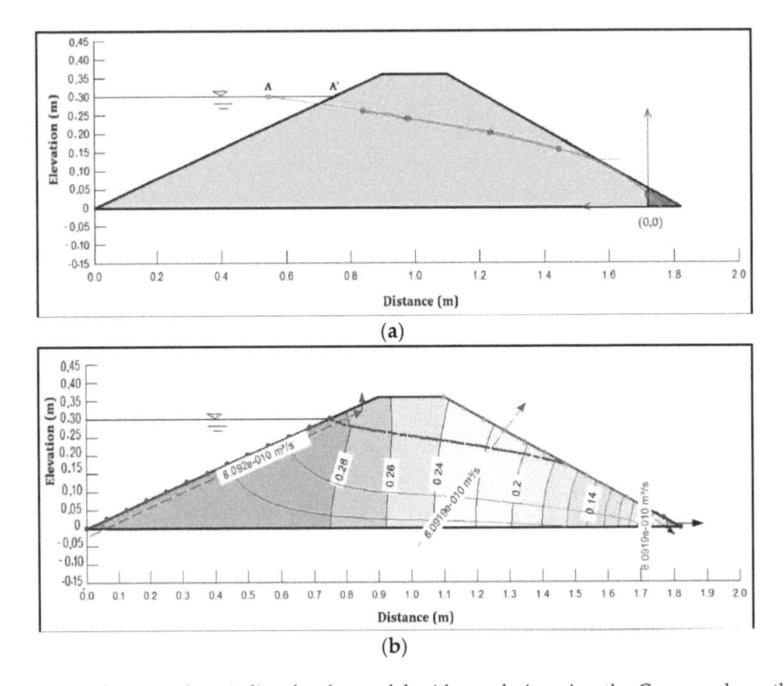


**Figure 5.** (**a**) Seepage phreatic line for the model with toe drain using the Casagrande method, (**b**) seepage line, flux at different points, and the contours of the total head for the model with toe drain, using the SEEP/W model.

Figure 5b shows the seepage line, flux at different points, and the contours of the total head using the SEEP/W model. From Figure 5b, the seepage flow rate is $q = 8.092 \times 10^{-10}$ m$^3$/s/m for well compacted soil. It is clear from Figure 5b that the seepage line touches the downstream face of the dam model between the distances of 1.46 to 1.7 m from the heel of the dam.

### *3.2. Earth-Fill Dam Model with Maximum Drain Length*

For the dam model with maximum drain length, observations revealed that the heights of phreatic line were 0.21, 0.201, 0.146, and 0.118 m for holes located in 0.87, 0.9, 1.04, and 1.1 from the heel of the dam models, respectively, while the phreatic line remained within the drain after 1.2 m from the heel. Thus, the observations confirmed that using horizontal drains prevent seepage from exiting the downstream of the dam model. The total seepage flow through the model is $2.2222 \times 10^{-7}$ (0.8 l/h) and the discharge of seepage is $4.441 \times 10^{-7}$ m$^3$/s/m.

From L. Casagrande solutions, the seepage losses through the dam were $q = 1.1259 \times 10^{-9}$ and $2.253 \times 10^{-7}$ m$^3$/s/m for well and low compacted soil, respectively, and the height of phreatic line were 0.2717, 0.225, 0.1574, and 0.0645 m for points located 0.66, 0.84, 1.04, and 1.2 m from the heel of the dam respectively (Figure 6a).

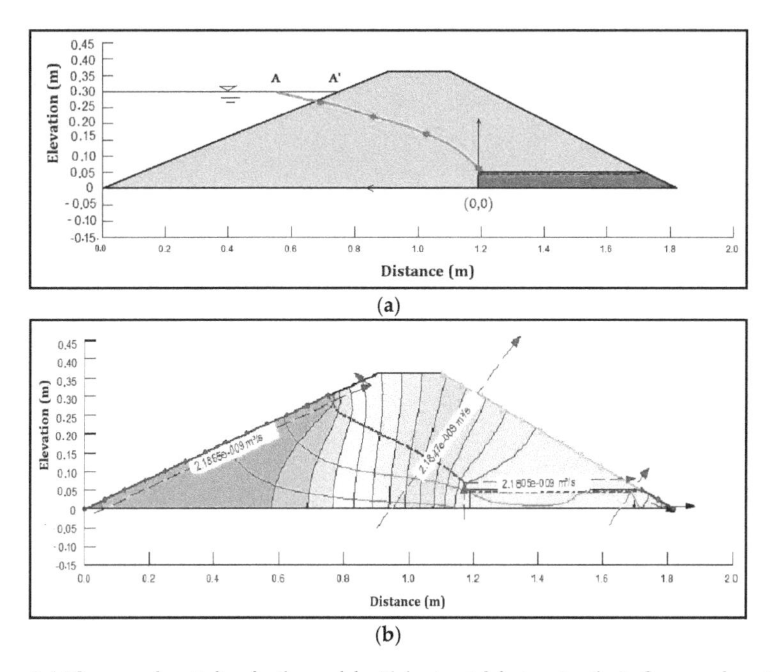


**Figure 6.** (**a**) Seepage phreatic line for the model with horizontal drain using the L. Casagrande method, (**b**) seepage line, flux at different points, and the contours of the total head for the model with horizontal drain, using the SEEP/W model.

The seepage line, flux, and the contours of the total head using the SEEP/W model are shown in Figure 6b, from which the seepage flow rate is $q = 2.1847 \times 10^{-9}$ m$^3$/s/m for well compacted soil.

## 4. Discussion

### *4.1. Comparison of Results From Experimental, Mathematical, and Numerical Methods*

The phreatic line for seepage through the two physical models using the three methods is presented in Figure 7. The results revealed that both L. Casagrande solutions and the SEEP/W model have a plotted seepage line compatible with the observed seepage line.

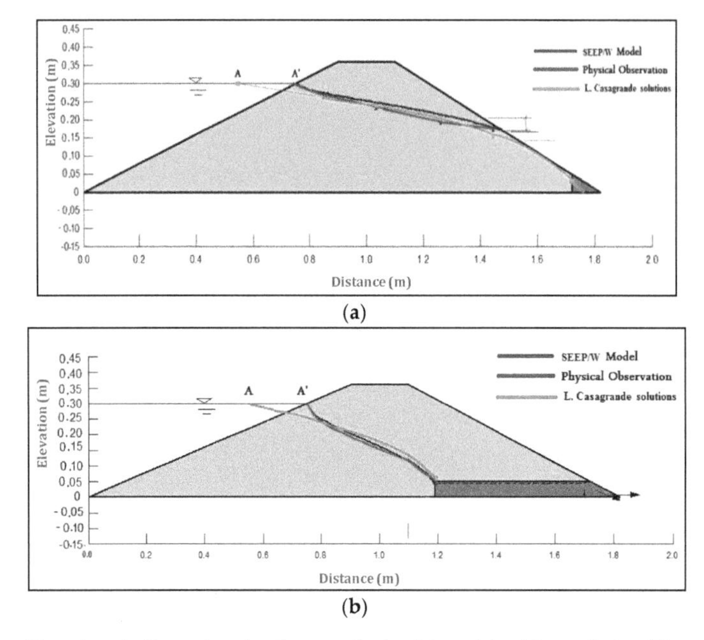


**Figure 7.** The phreatic line using the three methods: (**a**) model with toe drain, (**b**) model with horizontal drain.

The results of the seepage flow rate using the three methods are summarized in Table 1. As shown in the table, the seepage rate through the model with toe drain obtained from SEEP/W is close to that calculated by the L. Casagrande solution. However, the seepage rate observed from the physical model is higher than calculated with the other methods, even when considering low compacted soil. This difference in results indicates that when seepage flow intersects the downstream slope, water will exit the body of the dam and then follow the characteristics of surface water flow. Moreover, the intersection with downstream slope softens and weakens the soil mass, hence, increases the possibility of piping within the body of the physical dam model that eventually increases the total seepage rate.

For the model with horizontal drain, the seepage rate observed from the physical models is approximately the same as that obtained from SEEP/W and close to that calculated by the L. Casagrande solution when considering low compacted soil.

**Table 1.** Seepage flow rate using the three methods.

| **Models** | $q$ (m$^3$/s/m) | | | | |
|---|---|---|---|---|---|
| | **Physical** | **L. Casagrande** | | **SEEP/W** | |
| | | **Well Compacted** | **Low Compacted** | **Well Compacted** | **Low Compacted** |
| Toe drain | $1.277 \times 10^{-6}$ | $6.459 \times 10^{-10}$ | $1.292 \times 10^{-7}$ | $8.092 \times 10^{-10}$ | $1.621 \times 10^{-7}$ |
| Horizontal drain | $4.441 \times 10^{-7}$ | $1.126 \times 10^{-9}$ | $2.253 \times 10^{-7}$ | $2.185 \times 10^{-9}$ | $4.373 \times 10^{-7}$ |

### *4.2. Example of Seepage Analysis using SEEP/W Models*

The SEEP/W model was used to study seepage through a theoretical case of an earth-fill dam. The study consisted of analyzing seepage behavior with a total of 34 test trails through seven different configurations of a dam with 9 m height in order to recommend the most appropriate configuration based on seepage behavior. The seven dam configurations consisted of four homogenous dams and three zoned dams (Figures 8 and 9).

The four configurations of homogenous dams (Figure 8) consisted of toe drain, maximum length of horizontal drain of 16 m, minimum length of horizontal drain of 8 m, and medium length of horizontal drain of 12 m.

The three configurations of homogenous dams (Figure 9) consisted of a central core of 1:1 (H:V) for upstream (U/S) and downstream (D/S) slope, a central core of 1:0.5 (H:V) for upstream (U/s) and downstream (D/S) slope, and inclined cores of 1:1 and 1:0.5 (H:V) for upstream (U/S) and downstream (D/S) slope, respectively. Details of the seven configurations are presented in Table 2.

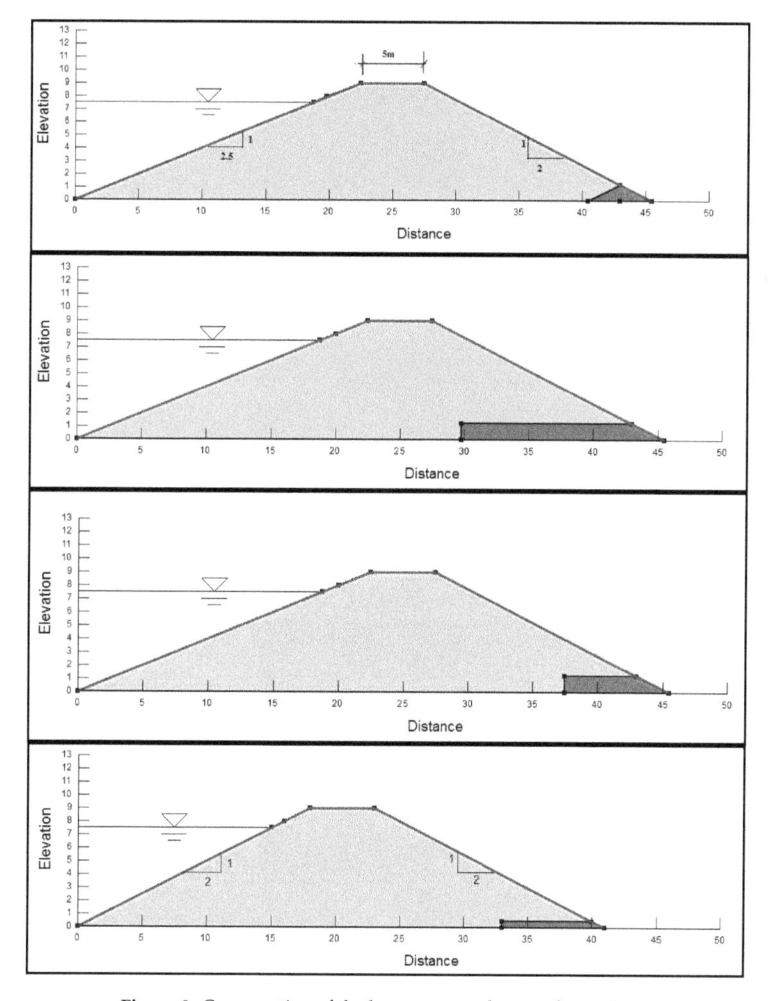


**Figure 8.** Cross section of the homogenous dam configurations.

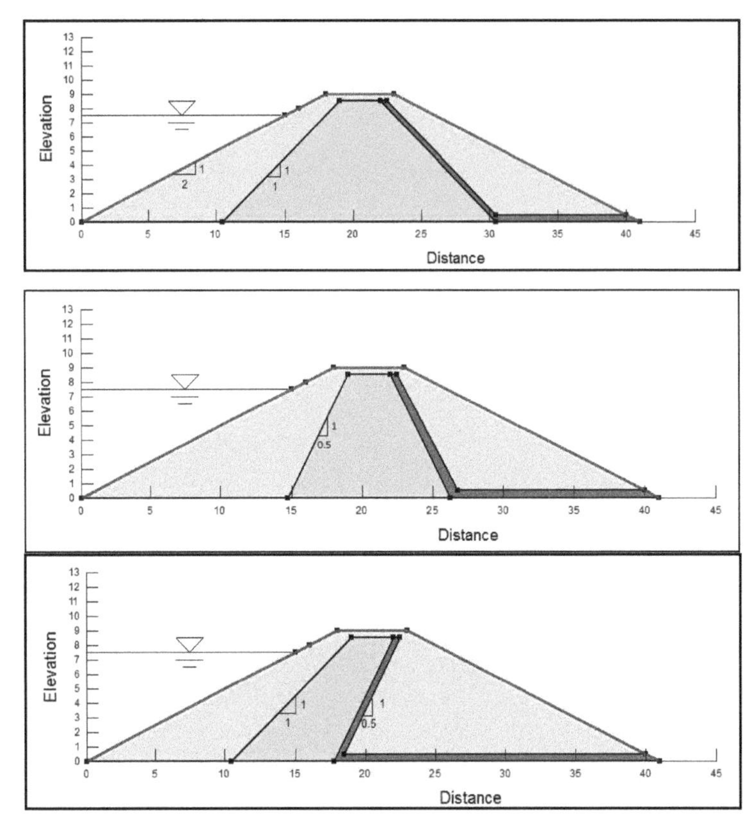


**Figure 9.** Cross section of the zoned dam configurations.

**Table 2.** Details of the seven configurations of the earth-fill dam.

| Design Details | Configuration | | | | | | |
|---|---|---|---|---|---|---|---|
| | (a) | (b) | (c) | (d) | (e) | (f) | (g) |
| **Type** | | **Homogenous** | | | | **Zoned** | |
| Height (m) | 9 | 9 | 9 | 9 | 9 | 9 | 9 |
| Crest W(m) | 5 | 5 | 5 | 5 | 5 | 5 | 5 |
| NFB (m) | 1.5 | 1.5 | 1.5 | 1.5 | 1.5 | 1.5 | 1.5 |
| U/S Slope (H:V) | 2.5:1 | 2.5:1 | 2.5:1 | 2:1 | 2:1 | 2:1 | 2:1 |
| D/S Slope (H:V) | 2:1 | 2:1 | 2:1 | 2:1 | 2:1 | 2:1 | 2:1 |
| Dam Material | ========== Silty sand ========== | | | | | - | |
| Shell | - | - | - | - | ===== Sand or gravel ===== | | |
| Core | - | - | - | - | ======= Silty sand ======= | | |
| Core type | - | - | - | - | Central | Central | Inclined |
| Core slope | - | - | - | - | 1:1 | 1:0.5 | 1:1 U/S<br>1:0.5 D/S |
| Core height | - | - | - | - | 8.5 | 8.5 | 8.5 |
| Core Crest | - | - | - | - | 3 | 3 | 3 |
| Type of drainage | Toe drain | Horizontal /Blanket (thickness of 1.25 and 0.5 m) | | | Chimney and horizontal | | |
| | | $L_{Max}$ = 16 m | $L_{Min}$ = 8 m | $L_{Mid}$ = 12 m | | | |

Table 3 shows the summary of results from the homogenous dam models. From the table, models with toe drain should be ignored because the seepage line either intersects with the downstream slope or have a very small space. Therefore, SEEP/W was unable to calculate seepage rates correctly. Model (b) is not preferable, because the seepage flow rate is very high. Model (c) is the best as its downstream cover of seepage is sufficient and has the lower seepage flow rate. Moreover, a medium drain length with 0.5 m thickness is preferable compared with 1.25 m thickness, because it is easier to construct and the difference in flow rate between them is insignificant.

**Table 3.** Details of seepage lines and rates from homogenous models.

| Models | Drain Details | Normal Water Level | | Maximum Water Level | |
|---|---|---|---|---|---|
| | | Seepage Line | Seepage $q$ ($m^3/s/m$) | Seepage line | Seepage $q$ ($m^3/s/m$) |
| a | Small toe drain (L = 2.5m) | Intersected | $3.817 \times 10^{-6}$ | Intersected | $3.265 \times 10^{-6}$ |
| | Toe drain (L = 5.0 m) | Small space | $4.395 \times 10^{-6}$ | Small space | $4.695 \times 10^{-6}$ |
| b | Drainage thickness = 1.25 m | OK | $7.55 \times 10^{-6}$ | OK | $9.244 \times 10^{-6}$ |
| | Drainage thickness = 0.5 m | OK | $7.655 \times 10^{-6}$ | OK | $9.3 \times 10^{-6}$ |
| c | Drainage thickness = 1.25 m | OK | $4.9 \times 10^{-6}$ | OK | $5.86 \times 10^{-6}$ |
| | Drainage thickness = 0.5 m | OK | $5.02 \times 10^{-6}$ | OK | $5.99 \times 10^{-6}$ |
| d | $L_{Mid}$ with 0.5 m thickness | OK | $5.23 \times 10^{-6}$ | OK | $6.18 \times 10^{-6}$ |
| | Toe drain | Intersected | $3.38 \times 10^{-6}$ | Intersected | $5.15 \times 10^{-6}$ |

Table 4 shows the summary of results from zoned dam models. As shown in the table, inclined core contains the smallest cross section area of core, but the seepage flow rate is very high compared with other models. The seepage flow rate for a central core with a 1:0.5 slope is slightly higher than the central core with a 1:1 slope, but the difference in cross section area makes it preferable.

**Table 4.** Details of seepage lines and rates from zoned models.

| Models | Core Detail | Required Core Material ($m^3/m$) | Shell Permeability | Normal Water Level | | Maximum Water Level | |
|---|---|---|---|---|---|---|---|
| | | | | Seepage Line | Seepage $q$ ($m^3/s/m$) | Seepage Line | Seepage $q$ ($m^3/s/m$) |
| e | Central 1:1 (H:V) | 97.75 | $K_{shell} = 10\ K_{core}$ | OK | $8.45 \times 10^{-6}$ | OK | $9.85 \times 10^{-6}$ |
| | | | $K_{shell} = 100\ K_{core}$ | OK | $8.73 \times 10^{-6}$ | OK | $1.01 \times 10^{-5}$ |
| | | | $K_{shell} = 1000\ K_{core}$ | OK | $8.75 \times 10^{-6}$ | OK | $1.02 \times 10^{-5}$ |
| f | Central 0.5:1 (H:V) | 61.63 | $K_{shell} = 10\ K_{core}$ | OK | $1.23 \times 10^{-5}$ | OK | $1.41 \times 10^{-5}$ |
| | | | $K_{shell} = 100\ K_{core}$ | OK | $1.16 \times 10^{-5}$ | OK | $1.51 \times 10^{-5}$ |
| | | | $K_{shell} = 1000\ K_{core}$ | OK | $1.32 \times 10^{-5}$ | OK | $1.48 \times 10^{-5}$ |
| g | Inclined | 43.56 | $K_{shell} = 10\ K_{core}$ | OK | $2.75 \times 10^{-5}$ | OK | $3.05 \times 10^{-5}$ |
| | | | $K_{shell} = 100\ K_{core}$ | OK | $2.9 \times 10^{-5}$ | OK | $3.24 \times 10^{-5}$ |
| | | | $K_{shell} = 1000\ K_{core}$ | OK | $2.62 \times 10^{-5}$ | OK | $3.41 \times 10^{-5}$ |

Based on the seepage analysis, it is concluded that if sufficient quantity of silty sand soil is available around the proposed dam location, homogenous earth-fill dam with medium drain length of 0.5 m thickness is the ideal design configuration. If there is not enough soil available, the zoned earth-fill dam with central core and 1:0.5 slope would be the optimum design criteria.

Although the physically based numerical methods have been certified capable of performing spatial and/or temporal simulation of certain systems, seepage flow through earth dams are still significantly affected by natural, random, and real-world conditions such as anisotropy and heterogeneity, thereby limiting their application. For instance, a dam's hydraulic conductivity can experience a deviation from the designed value due to operation or construction-related problems. Such situation demands the use of physical-based models to determine the model inputs and the associated output predictions before introducing other simulation models. This case is particularly when there are not enough field data and thus an accurate prediction is desired when conceiving the physics [35,36].

## 5. Conclusions

The study of seepage through earth-fill dams is very important for constructed dams to ensure that the control of seepage is sufficient for the safe and sustainable operation of the dam. It is also important in the design and construction of new dams to ensure that the seepage through and under the dam will be well controlled. In this study, the experimental and numerical analyses of seepage through earth-fill dam models were conducted. Results from two physical models were compared with those obtained from L. Casagrande equations and the SEEP/W program. Comparisons revealed that the location of the seepage line obtained from the three methods was almost the same. Moreover, when the seepage flow intersects the downstream slope and piping takes place, using SEEP/W to calculate flow rate becomes useless as it cannot calculate the volume of water flow in pipes. This was revealed by the big difference in the results between physical and numerical models in the first physical model, while the results were compatible in the second physical model when the seepage line stayed within the body of dam and low compacted soil was adopted. The results have proven the importance of using horizontal drains to control the phreatic line position for the stability of earth dams, as touching the downstream slope would soften and weaken the soil mass and increase the potential piping. Seven different dam configurations at normal and maximum water levels have been studied (four homogenous and three zoned dams) to find the most appropriate configuration among them, according to seepage analysis. Seepage analysis revealed that if a sufficient quantity of silty sand soil is available around the proposed dam location, a homogenous earth-fill dam with medium drain length of 0.5 m thickness is the best design configuration. Otherwise, a zoned earth-fill dam with a central core and 1:0.5 (H:V) is recommended.

**Author Contributions:** Conceptualization, Z.M.Y., A.H.G., A.M.S.A.-J., Y.M.G., and N.A.-A.; Data curation, A.M.S.A.-J.; Formal analysis, Z.M.Y., A.M.S.A.-J., Y.M.G., H.A.A., and N.A.-A.; Investigation, Z.M.Y., A.H.G., A.M.S.A.-J., and Y.M.G.; Methodology, A.M.S.A.-J.; Project administration, Z.M.Y.; Resources, A.H.G.; Supervision, A.H.G., Y.M.G., and N.A.-A.; Validation, A.M.S.A.-J. and H.A.A.; Visualization, A.M.S.A.-J., Y.M.G., and H.A.A.; Writing—original draft, Z.M.Y., A.H.G., A.M.S.A.-J., Y.M.G., H.A.A., and N.A.-A.; Writing—review and editing, Z.M.Y., A.H.G., A.M.S.A.-J., Y.M.G., H.A.A., and N.A.-A. All authors have read and agreed to the published version of the manuscript.

**Funding:** This research received no external funding.

**Conflicts of Interest:** The authors declare no conflicts of interest.

## References

1. Graf, W.L. Dam nation: A geographic census of american dams and their large-scale hydrologic impacts. *Water Resour. Res.* **1999**. [CrossRef]
2. Sayl, K.N.; Muhammad, N.S.; Yaseen, Z.M.; El-Shafie, A. Estimation the Physical Variables of Rainwater Harvesting System Using Integrated GIS-Based Remote Sensing Approach. *Water Resour. Manag.* **2016**, *30*, 3299–3313. [CrossRef]
3. Yener Ozkan, M. A review of considerations on seismic safety of embankments and earth and rock-fill dams. *Soil Dyn. Earthq. Eng.* **1998**. [CrossRef]
4. Chahar, B.R. Determination of Length of a Horizontal Drain in Homogeneous Earth Dams. *J. Irrig. Drain. Eng.* **2004**, *130*, 530–536. [CrossRef]
5. Yaseen, Z.M.; Ameen, A.M.S.; Aldlemy, M.S.; Ali, M.; Abdulmohsin Afan, H.; Zhu, S.; Sami Al-Janabi, A.M.; Al-Ansari, N.; Tiyasha, T.; Tao, H. State-of-the Art-Powerhouse, Dam Structure, and Turbine Operation and Vibrations. *Sustainability* **2020**, *12*, 1676. [CrossRef]
6. Richards, K.S.; Reddy, K.R. Critical appraisal of piping phenomena in earth dams. *Bull. Eng. Geol. Environ.* **2007**. [CrossRef]
7. Calamak, M.; Yanmaz, A.M. Probabilistic assessment of slope stability for earth-fill dams having random soil parameters. In Proceedings of the 5th IAHR International Symposium on Hydraulic Structures, Brisbane, Australia, 25–28 September 2014; Engineers Australia: Barton, Australia, 2014.
8. Athani, S.S.; Solanki, C.H.; Dodagoudar, G.R. Seepage and Stability Analyses of Earth Dam Using Finite Element Method. *Aquat. Procedia* **2015**. [CrossRef]

9. Fell, R.; Wan, C.F.; Cyganiewicz, J.; Foster, M. Time for development of internal erosion and piping in embankment dams. *J. Geotech. Geoenviron. Eng.* **2003**. [CrossRef]
10. Özer, A.T.; Bromwell, L.G. Stability assessment of an earth dam on silt/clay tailings foundation: A case study. *Eng. Geol.* **2012**. [CrossRef]
11. Riahi-Madvar, H.; Dehghani, M.; Akib, S.; Shamshirband, S.; Chau, K. Developing a mathematical framework in preliminary designing of detention rockfill dams for flood peak reduction. *Eng. Appl. Comput. Fluid Mech.* **2019**. [CrossRef]
12. Al-Janabi, A.M.S.; Ghazali, A.H.; Yusuf, B.; Mohammed, T.A. Permeable channel cross section for maximizing stormwater infiltration and seepage rates. *J. Irrig. Drain. Eng.* **2018**, *144*. [CrossRef]
13. Erfeng, Z.; Ji, L.; Yufeng, J. The seepage evolution law under the fault creep in right bank of Longyangxia Dam. *Eng. Fail. Anal.* **2014**. [CrossRef]
14. Jassam, M.G.; Abdulrazzaq, S.S. Theoretical Analysis of Seepage through Homogeneous and Non-homogeneous Saturated-Unsaturated Soil. *J. Eng.* **2019**, *25*, 52–67. [CrossRef]
15. Kermani, E.; Barani, G. Seepage Analysis through Earth Dam Based on Finite Difference Method. *J. Basic Appl. Sci. Res.* **2012**, *2*, 11621–11625.
16. Al-Janabi, A.M.S. Study of Seepage through Earth-Fill Dam Using Physical and Numerical Models. Master's Thesis, University Putra Malaysia, Seri Kembangan, Malaysia, 2013.
17. Phatak, D.R.; Pathak, S.R.; Birid, K.C. Estimation of Phreatic Line Using Dimensional Analysis. In Proceedings of the Fifth International Conference on Case Histories in Geotechnical Engineering, New York, NY, USA, 13–17 April 2004.
18. Stello, M.W. Seepage Charts for Homogeneous and Zoned Embankments. *J. Geotech. Eng.* **1987**, *113*, 996–1012. [CrossRef]
19. Casagrande, A. Seepage Through Dams. *J. N. Engl. Water Works Assoc.* **1937**, *1*, 131–172.
20. Chen, S.; Zhong, Q.; Cao, W. Breach mechanism and numerical simulation for seepage failure of earth-rock dams. *Sci. China Technol. Sci.* **2012**. [CrossRef]
21. Cho, S.E. Probabilistic analysis of seepage that considers the spatial variability of permeability for an embankment on soil foundation. *Eng. Geol.* **2012**. [CrossRef]
22. Mansuri, B.; Salmasi, F. Effect of Horizontal Drain Length and Cutoff Wall on Seepage and Uplift Pressure in Heterogeneous Earth Dam with Numerical Simulation. *J. Civil Eng. Urban.* **2013**, *3*, 114–121.
23. Alekseevich, A.N.; Sergeevich, A.A. Numerical modelling of tailings dam thermal-seepage regime considering phase transitions. *Model. Simul. Eng.* **2017**. [CrossRef]
24. Sivakumar, G.L.; Vasudevan, A.K. Seepage velocity and piping resistance of coir fiber mixed soils. *J. Irrig. Drain. Eng.* **2008**. [CrossRef]
25. Hofmann, J.R.; Hofmann, P.A. Darcy' s Law and Structural Explanation in Hydrology. In *PSA: Proceedings of the Biennial Meeting of the Philosophy of Science Association*; The University of Chicago Press: Chicago, IL, USA, 1992; Volume 1, pp. 23–35.
26. Sherard, J.L.; Woodward, R.J.; Gizienski, S.J. *Earth and Earth Rock Dams: Engineering Problems of Design and Construction*; John Wiley & Sons Inc: Hoboken, NJ, USA, 1963; ISBN 9780471785477.
27. Das, B.M. *Advanced Soil Mechanics*, 5th ed.; CRC Press: Boca Raton, FL, USA, 2019; ISBN 9781351215176.
28. Malekpour, A.; Farsadizadeh, D.; Hosseinzadeh Dalir, A.; Sadrekarimi, J. Effect of horizontal drain size on the stability of an embankment dam in steady and transient seepage conditions. *Turk. J. Eng. Environ. Sci.* **2012**, *36*, 139–152. [CrossRef]
29. Vaskinn, K.A.; Løvoll, A.; Höeg, K.; Morris, M.; Hanson, G.J.; Hassan, M.A. Physical modeling of breach formation: Large scale field tests. *Prec. Dam Saf.* **2004**, 1–16. Available online: https://pdfs.semanticscholar.org/29c4/fc2938493ad843240e87a6a63e9d1633847b.pdf (accessed on 22 March 2020).
30. Chahar, B.R.; Graillot, D.; Gaur, S. Storm-Water Management through Infiltration Trenches. *J. Irrig. Drain. Eng.* **2012**, *138*, 274–281. [CrossRef]
31. Abdul Jabbar Jamel, A.; Ibrahim Ali, M. Influence of Cavity Under Hydraulic Structures on Seepage Characteristics. *Int. J. Eng. Technol.* **2018**, *7*, 461. [CrossRef]
32. Ullah, A.; Kassim, A.; Alam, I.; Junaid, M.; Ahmad, I.S. Efficiency analysis of seepage of Baz Ali small dam, Kurram Agency using clay blanket and cut-off wall with sand filter. *Bull. Geol. Soc. Malays.* **2019**, *67*, 113–118. [CrossRef]

33. Chahar, B.R. Closure to "Determination of Length of a Horizontal Drain in Homogeneous Earth Dams" by Bhagu R. Chahar. *J. Irrig. Drain. Eng.* **2006**, *132*, 89–90. [CrossRef]
34. Casagrande, A. Seepage through dams. *Natl. Acad. Sci. Eng. Med.* **1937**, *51*, 131–172.
35. Pham-Van, S.; Hinkelmann, R.; Nehrig, M.; Martinez, I. A comparison of model concepts and experiments for seepage processes through a dike with a fault zone. *Eng. Appl. Comput. Fluid Mech.* **2011**. [CrossRef]
36. Yaseen, Z.M.; Sulaiman, S.O.; Deo, R.C.; Chau, K.-W. An enhanced extreme learning machine model for river flow forecasting: State-of-the-art, practical applications in water resource engineering area and future research direction. *J. Hydrol.* **2018**, *569*, 387–408. [CrossRef]

*Article*

# Developing a Methodological Framework for Estimating Temporary Drainage Capacity to Inform Land Requirements for a Highway Construction Project in Scotland

**Mandy Wallace [1,2,*], Anita Meldrum [2], Slobodan Mickovski [2], Iain McNee , Derwyn Lear [3] and Sam Flint [3]**

1. People and Places Solutions, Transportation, Jacobs UK Ltd., Glasgow G2 7HX, UK; iain.mcnee@jacobs.com
2. Department of Civil Engineering and Environment, School of Computing, Engineering and Built Environment, Glasgow Caledonian University, Glasgow G4 0BA, UK; anita.meldrum@gcu.ac.uk (A.M.); Slobodan.mickovski@gcu.ac.uk (S.M.)
3. Formerly Jacobs UK Ltd., Glasgow G2 7HX, UK; derwyn.lear@gavia-environmental.co.uk (D.L.); samuel.flint@defra.gov.uk (S.F.)

* Correspondence: mandy.wallace@jacobs.com

Received: 26 May 2020; Accepted: 29 June 2020; Published: 8 July 2020

**Abstract:** Silt pollution generated during major highway construction projects can prove detrimental to the water environment and the aquatic species that depend on it. Construction activities can leave many kilometers of exposed soil susceptible to erosion from surface water runoff, which can result in silt pollution and degradation of ecologically sensitive watercourses if appropriate mitigation is not in place. In Scotland, assurances need to be provided during scheme development to demonstrate that there is sufficient space to accommodate temporary drainage. In response, a methodological framework has been developed that can be applied before construction commences to estimate the required capacity of settlement ponds including runoff and soil loss volume estimation, which are estimated using the Rational Method and Revised Universal Soil Loss Equation (RUSLE). The application of the framework as a case-study has demonstrated the potential applicability of the approach and highlighted where further refinements can be made to increase the robustness for future applications by improving the accuracy of input parameters to address site-specific conditions. Furthermore, it demonstrates how adopting erosion control measures can reduce the land required to accommodate temporary settlement ponds.

**Keywords:** highway construction; environmental protection; soil loss; erosion control

---

## 1. Introduction

Highways construction can be detrimental to the environment due to the level of ground disturbance, which can span many kilometers. Once vegetated surfaces are stripped and topsoil is removed, areas of exposed soil are left susceptible to water and wind erosion. When exposed surfaces are eroded, without adequate water management in place, suspended eroded materials can enter the water environment. Once in the water environment, they can be damaging to downstream receptors [1]. Providing suitable mitigation against elevated rates of suspended solids in the water environment prevents a number of ecologically detrimental effects. This can include reduced light penetration in the water column for aquatic plants and smothering of salmonid spawning areas [2].

When considering water and pollution control in a construction context, it is necessary to consider both erosion and sediment control [1]. Soil erosion is a natural process where the soil surface is eroded by water, wind, ice and gravity. The issue is exacerbated during construction through the removal of vegetation, which leaves the underlying bare surface exposed and increases the rate of erosion [3]. Controlling runoff and soil stabilization are both forms of erosion control [4] that should be considered as preventative measures. Incorporating suitable preventative measures should be considered as a vital first step as they are the most effective at preventing the mobilization of clay and silt particles [5] and help reduce the rate of soil erosion [2].

Sediment control is required once eroded soil particles are suspended in runoff. The aim of sediment control measures is to facilitate the settlement of eroded material, or removal by filtration before the eroded material discharges from site [4]. Examples of sediment control include buffer strips, temporary sediment basins and tanks, silt fences and biodegradable fiber rolls [2]. As recommended, sediment control should be considered as the second step, as reliance upon sediment controls will be reduced through effective erosion control [5]. When using temporary settlement ponds, the surface area should be 1.5% of the catchment it serves to achieve in the region of 90% total solid reduction although solids reduction in a highway construction environment can be in the region of 15% [5,6]. Even with results as effective as 90% total solid reduction, if fine particles are present, then sufficient settlement may never be achieved [1,7,8]. Therefore, temporary settlement ponds should be used in conjunction with other control measures [5,8], including erosion controls such as vegetation, geotextiles and mulch [5]. In addition to the variable treatment efficiency and relatively large footprint needed for effective settlement, relying solely on sediment control can prove to be more costly compared to minimizing soil loss as a priority [1].

The Design Manual for Roads and Bridges (DMRB) [9] sets out three stages of assessment reporting. Design organizations follow this staged process to provide statutory and public bodies with the necessary information in relation to the environmental, economic and traffic effects of the proposed scheme and alternative proposals under consideration. The Stage 3 assessment clearly identifies the advantages and disadvantages of the preferred route and includes an assessment of the likely significant environmental effects [9]. During the Stage 3 assessment for a linear highway construction project in Scotland [10], the environmental regulator, a statutory consultee, requested confirmation that there was sufficient available land to accommodate temporary drainage to effectively manage runoff from the site prior to discharge into the water environment. From this request, it became apparent that there was a need to agree an effective framework approach to calculate the required capacity of temporary drainage during construction. Developing a framework allows stakeholders to establish that there is sufficient available land to accommodate the temporary drainage measures and deliver the necessary environmental mitigation to protect the water environment.

Methodological frameworks provide an approach to reach a desired outcome whilst incorporating necessary parameters needed to meet regulatory requirements. Within an environmental context, methodological frameworks have been developed for a range of purposes including: protecting wetlands from negative effects associated with linear development projects [11]; soil erosion risk assessment [12]; developing a sustainability assessment for eco-engineering measures [13]; combining digital and environmental data to identify catchment boundaries [14]; and predicting soil loss using the Revised Universal Soil Loss Equation (RUSLE) [15]. To be effective, the developed framework needs to include the parameters required for temporary drainage. It was decided that the methodological approach would incorporate the design considerations provided in [1]. This is an industry-wide source of information for protecting the water environment during highway construction and is regarded by the environmental regulator as a source of best-practice measures [16]. This includes using runoff volume estimation and the RUSLE [17] to calculate sediment input into control options, which include temporary settlement ponds.

To the best of our knowledge, there are no standardized approaches to calculate the capacity of temporary drainage features when compared to drainage systems that will serve the operational phase of a highway. The flood risk policy in Scotland [18] requires that all new infrastructure and buildings should be designed to avoid surface water flooding from 1:200-year (0.5% annual exceedance probability (AEP)) rainfall events. However, sizing temporary drainage systems to accommodate the 1:200-year event is an overly conservative approach due to the length of time that temporary drainage would be in operation, which would generally be less than five years. Designing temporary drainage to accommodate a 1:10-year rainfall event has been the accepted design standard based on the recommendation set out in industry guidance because the duration of construction is generally less than 10 years [1]. However, it should be noted that in Scotland, the environmental regulator would expect to see a minimum of a 1:10-year event used for temporary drainage depending on the anticipated timescale for construction [19].

The Universal Soil Loss Equation (USLE) [20] was developed to provide a prediction tool. It is used to calculate long-time average soil losses due to surface water runoff, in a specific area under specific field crop and management scenarios. The potential application of (R)USLE in the construction industry was introduced when the authors presented the concept that the USLE could be diversified for use in the construction industry [20]. A number of states in the USA currently apply the RUSLE to calculate sediment yield [4,21]. Several studies have applied the (R)USLE in a highway construction setting in various global locations [22–24]. Other studies have also used RUSLE to estimate soil loss rates at the continental scale [25], including consideration of seasonal variability [26]. However, outside the USA, difficulties can arise in the selection of the most representative input data [27]. Furthermore, exposed subsoils can have different characteristics than the topsoil which further complicates the selection of representative input values [20] without site specific geotechnical data.

The importance of developing a framework for estimating temporary drainage capacity has been further highlighted with the release of guidance by the environmental regulator to assist responsible parties in the preparation of Pollution Prevention Plans (PPPs). PPPs are required to obtain a Construction Site License (CSL) from the environmental regulator before major construction projects can commence [28]. There is now an urgent need for those responsible for the construction and delivery of major infrastructure schemes to address the high risk of pollution to avoid potential enforcement action. In this context, high risk of pollution associated with highway construction is linked with silted water runoff from exposed soils, material stockpiles and road runoff, where the absence or inadequacies of mitigation measures adopted during the construction phase can lead to environmental pollution.

The aim of this study is to set out the methodological framework used by Jacobs [29] for estimating the capacity of temporary drainage, to inform land requirements. This includes the application of the framework on a current highway construction project as a case-study.

## 2. Materials and Methods

### 2.1. Methodological Framework Development

Providing assurance during scheme development that sufficient space will be available for temporary drainage is a relatively new concept, as this would have been the responsibility of the appointed contractor. This was on the assumed basis that permanent sustainable drainage system (SuDS) basin locations would be used during construction to accommodate temporary settlement ponds due to the available land to accommodate a 1 in 200-year rainfall event.

Across the industry in Scotland, consultants are using various approaches to assess if sufficient land is available for temporary drainage. The approaches include treatment volume estimation [30] and a combination of estimated runoff and soil loss volume using USLE [1]. Jacobs [29] have proceeded with the approach using runoff volume estimation and estimated soil loss using the USLE. This would be achieved by using a combination of geographic information systems (GIS) [31] and calculations. The outputs of this approach will provide a method for calculating the size of temporary drainage features (settlement ponds).

#### 2.1.1. Construction Phasing and Catchment Delineation

Large linear construction projects are typically constructed in phases, which can minimise disruptive impacts for road users and neighboring communities [32]. Constructing in phases creates temporary drainage catchments dependent on topography and suitable discharge locations. Five-meter airborne-derived LiDAR survey data was obtained during early scheme preparation stages. LiDAR data has been used in other studies to produce a Digital Terrain Model (DTM) at a 1 m resolution to identify landscape features and surface flow pathways [33] and at a 5 m resolution (DTMs) for catchment delineation [34]. However, as construction works commence, the land profile is changed, and the level of detail captured in the DTM can be lost. In addition, inaccuracies can exist in the vertical and horizontal resolution [34]. To mitigate against the risk of DTM inaccuracies, the DTM would be compared to total station topographical survey data (1:500) obtained as part of the highway construction project preparation, as well as 1:10,000 Ordnance Survey mapping.

2.1.2. Soil Loss Estimation

To estimate soil loss, the Revised Universal Soil Loss Equation (RUSLE) [17] has been incorporated into the methodological framework, which is a suggested approach in UK industry guidance [1].

$$A = R \times K \times (LS) \times C \times P \tag{1}$$

where: A = soil loss per annum (t ha$^{-1}$ yr$^{-1}$); R = rainfall factor (MJ mm ha$^{-1}$ h$^{-1}$ yr$^{-1}$); K = soil erodibility factor (t ha h ha$^{-1}$ MJ$^{-1}$ mm$^{-1}$); and LS = slope factor (horizontal slope and gradient, unitless]; C = cover factor (unitless) and P = erosion control practice (unitless).

The R factor (average annual rainfall–runoff erosivity) is an assimilation of energy and intensity factors. The energy component reflects raindrop size, and intensity is the maximum intensity over a 30-min time-period [4]. The erodibility factor (K), is a numerical approximation of the commonly adopted nomograph [20], which incorporates soil parameters including particle size distribution and organic matter content, permeability and structure [20]. These include soil texture, organic matter content and soil structure and permeability to provide an annual soil loss volume. The LS factor is the topographical representation in the RUSLE that captures the slope length and gradient [17]. The calculation of this factor is achievable using GIS [31]. This approach calculates a LS factor for each cell within a GIS raster and the mean value for each drainage catchment can then be obtained using the zonal statistics produced.

The cover (C) and practice (P) factors can be used to identify effects that different cropping and mechanical management options will have on soil loss [17]; have been omitted for the purposes of this study. This decision was made based on the C and P factor values provided in [1], which are 1 for bare soils. These factors were deemed to be representative of conditions following site clearance on a highway construction site. In reference to Equation 1, the inclusion of C and P factors of 1 would not alter the estimated soil loss volume (A). However, as C and P factors can strongly influence soil loss, their inclusion and refinement warrant further consideration for future framework refinements.

2.1.3. Runoff Volume Estimation

Runoff volume estimation was carried out by using the Rational Method [35,36] which can be used to calculate the peak discharge rate from a catchment [37]. This approach requires input parameters, which include the contributing area (catchment size), rainfall depth and a dimensionless runoff coefficient, which reflects the proportion of peak discharge in relation to direct storm runoff [37]. The selection of the runoff coefficient is dependent on catchment surface characteristics [37,38] and failing to select appropriate coefficient(s) that represent catchment characteristics can limit the accuracy of the Rational Method [38]. Examples of published runoff coefficients [37] include 0.25–0.95 for urban and suburban developed areas and 0.05–0.35 for grassed areas, depending on slope gradient and soil. This approach allows for the volume of water that needs to be attenuated in a temporary drainage feature (i.e., a settlement pond), to be estimated.

This approach can be applied to individual catchments, such as those reflecting phased construction, to calculate the runoff volumes requiring attenuation. In addition, applying this approach on a linear construction site allows selection of different rainfall and permeability coefficients dependent upon the geographic reach of the project and location of each catchment.

#### 2.1.4. Temporary Drainage Sizing

To be effective, temporary drainage must have adequate capacity to accommodate the runoff volume generated in the contributing area served by the drainage feature. In addition, there must be sufficient capacity to account for the loss of storage volume from eroded soil transported to the drainage feature in runoff. To achieve this, the runoff volume calculated per drainage catchment using the Rational Method and soil loss using USLE have been incorporated into Equation (2).

$$Vt = Qp + K \tag{2}$$

where: Vt = treatment volume ($m^3$); Qp = runoff volume ($m^3$); K = soil loss ($m^3$/3 months).

The RUSLE calculates soil loss per annum. However, in reality, construction sites are dynamic, and it is not uncommon for frequent changes to construction layouts to meet the demands on site. Based on this, it is unlikely that a temporary drainage feature would remain in operation for a year. Therefore, soil loss (K, Equation (2)) has been amended to provide a soil loss estimate for a three-month period and converted to provide a soil loss volume in $m^3$.

### *2.2. Methodological Framework Application to Study Site*

#### 2.2.1. Site Information

The methodological framework has been applied to a proposed 8.2 km section of the A9 Dualling scheme between Tay Crossing and Ballinluig, Perthshire, Scotland (Figure 1). The scheme is located primarily within the extent of the River Tay floodplain. The River Tay Catchment includes the River Tay and several tributaries, which are included in the River Tay Special Area of Conservation (SAC). The SAC designation is based on the presence of species including Atlantic salmon, Lamprey (brook, river and sea) and otter [39].

Available site information [32] indicates that the site is underlain with humus iron podzols derived from glaciofluvial sand and gravel. Superficial deposits primarily consist of alluvium (clay, silt, sand and gravel) and glaciofluvial deposits of gravel, sand, silt and clay, with isolated areas of river terrace deposits along the existing A9.

The proposed construction project will include the widening of the existing single carriageway over 7.7 km with a 0.5 km single carriageway section at the southern extent, which will tie in with the existing single carriageway to form a dual carriageway. The design includes earthworks comprising ten sections of cutting and four sections of embankment. Anticipated slope gradients range from 1V:2H to 1V:3H with the exception of a soil-nailed steepened slope, at an angle of 70 degrees [32].

#### 2.2.2. Construction Phasing and Catchment Delineation

For this case-study, the construction project has been split into three phases [32]. Using available LiDAR data obtained during earlier scheme preparations, a Digital Terrain Model (DTM) was produced using GIS. Individual drainage catchments were identified based on the topography and categorised based on the anticipated phasing of the construction works. Catchments have been represented by a polygon feature shapefile and the corresponding catchment area has been extracted to calculate runoff and soil loss volumes for each catchment. This approach allows for a bespoke approach to sizing construction drainage features that will be required to attenuate and treat runoff generated within each catchment.

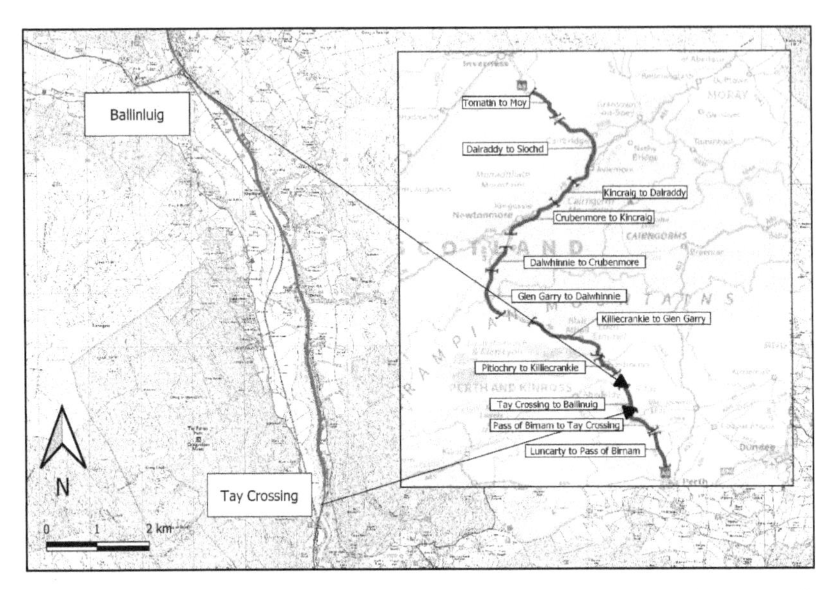


**Figure 1.** Study site for methodological framework application with extract of the A9 dualling project extent.

2.2.3. Soil Loss Estimation

The input parameters for the R, K and LS factors have been derived from literature sources and GIS software (Table 1). A uniform R factor value has been applied based on [1], which was derived from an isoderant map [20]. In this instance, the R factor is a multi-annual average index which has been calculated using 22-year rainfall records where any rainfall events < 12.7 mm are omitted unless > 6.35 mm of rain was recorded in 15 min. It is worth noting that the R factor does not include the erosive-force-associated runoff generated during thawing, snow melt, or irrigation [20]. A uniform K factor has been applied to each catchment based on engineering judgement (Table 1). The K factor selected was based on factors published in [40], which represented a material with a silt loam texture with 2% organic matter content. As the site is located primarily within the River Tay floodplain, the decision was made to uniformly apply the K factor to provide a conservative assumption of erodibility, based on the presence of alluvium.

**Table 1.** Input parameters for runoff and soil loss estimation.

| Parameter | Input Value | Unit | Source |
|---|---|---|---|
| | RUSLE | | |
| R factor | 100 | - | [20] |
| K factor | 0.42 | - | [40] |
| LS factor | Catchment specific | - | [31] |
| C & P | - | - | Not included |
| | Catchment Runoff Volume Estimation | | |
| Rainfall depth (10-year 6 h) | 43.9 | mm | [41] |
| Permeability factor | 0.6 | - | [1] |
| Catchment area | Catchment specific | ha | - |

Note: Where R factor, rainfall factor; K factor, soil erodibility factor; LS factor, slope factor; C factor, cover factor, and P factor, erosion control factor.

LS factors have been calculated using each individual temporary drainage catchment (Section 2.2.2). A slope grid was created from the 5 m DTM, then the approach set out by [31] was used to calculate mean LS factors for each catchment.

#### 2.2.4. Runoff Volume Estimation

Runoff volume estimation has been calculated using several contributing factors, including catchment size, rainfall and the runoff coefficient. The input parameters used in this study are provided in Table 1. The rainfall depth used is for a 10-year, 6-h event from Guay (NGR 299800, 749100), which is approximately at the mid-point of the scheme. The rainfall depth was obtained from the Flood Estimation Handbook web service using FEH13 peaks over threshold values [41].

The permeability factors provided in [1] range between 1 (impermeable surface with complete conversion of rainfall to runoff) and 0.4–0.75, which would be typical of a stripped construction site and dependent upon the infiltration capacity of the underlying soil. Owing to the sites location in the River Tay floodplain, a permeability factor of 0.6 was applied across all catchments, based on engineering judgement. This assumes that each catchment area would be entirely stripped, leaving the ground surface exposed so other catchment land use and runoff coefficient(s) [37] would not be required.

#### 2.2.5. Treatment Volume Estimation

To provide the necessary capacity to accommodate the 1 in 10-year design rainfall event, the settlement ponds must have sufficient capacity to accommodate the runoff volume and sediment accumulations. On this basis, the capacity is determined using Equation (2), which is applied to each delineated drainage catchment with pond depths assumed to be 1 m. This provides a conservative approach by incorporating the soil loss estimation for a 3-month period. However, to maintain this capacity, it will be necessary to routinely maintain the settlement ponds, with sediment accumulations removed, as a minimum, every 3 months. Failure to do so would increase the risk that the settlement ponds would not have sufficient capacity to attenuate runoff volumes for rainfall events below the 1 in 10-year design standard. At this stage, pond depths have been assumed to be a maximum of 1 m to avoid overly deep ponds that would not facilitate settlement.

#### 2.2.6. Land Requirements

The required land within each drainage catchment to accommodate construction drainage has been estimated using treatment volume (Equations (2) and (3)).

$$LR = Vt \div \text{catchment area} \times 100 \tag{3}$$

where: LR = land requirements (% of total catchment area, assuming 1 m pond depth); Vt = treatment volume ($m^3$) and catchment area ($m^2$).

## 3. Results

### 3.1. Methodological Framework Development

A methodological framework (Figure 2) has been developed to meet the requirements of the environmental regulator. The framework has been used to estimate the required capacity of construction drainage features, to inform the allocation of space required during construction. Owing to the processes underpinning the development of the LS factor, the methodological process used is illustrated separately (Figure 3).

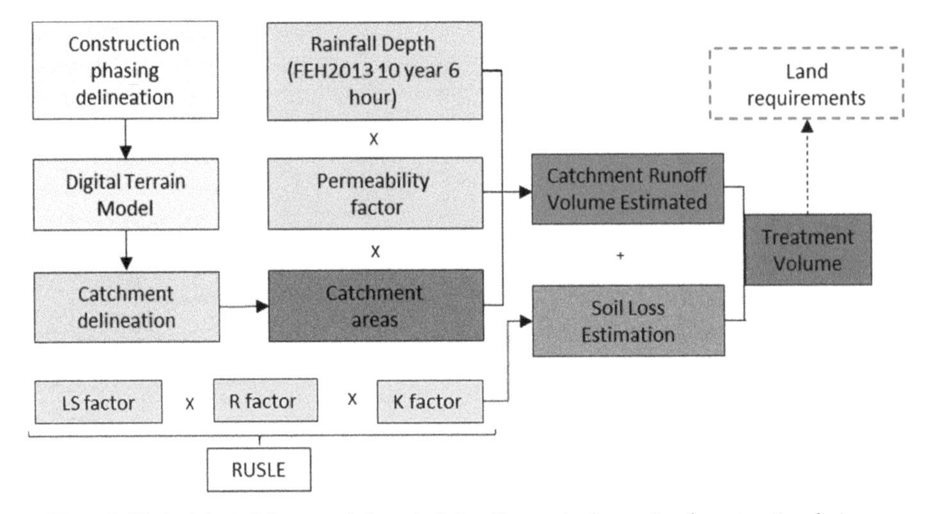


**Figure 2.** Methodological framework for calculating the required capacity of construction drainage ponds, which includes runoff volume and soil loss estimation.

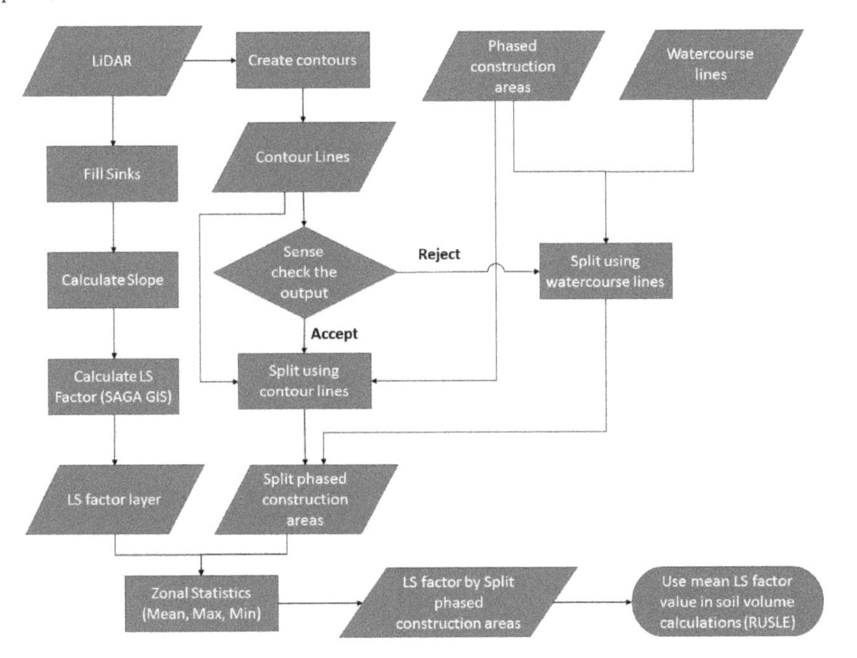


**Figure 3.** Methodological process for deriving the LS factor for estimating soil loss using RUSLE.

### 3.2. *Application to Study Site*

The methodological framework has been applied to a proposed highway construction project. A summary of the results generated following the application of the methodological framework is provided in Table 2. This includes catchment size, runoff volume, soil loss volume per 3-month period, and the corresponding treatment volume for each anticipated construction phase. Also included is the percentage of treatment volume to accommodate the estimated soil loss and the percentage of catchment area required to accommodate the total treatment volume, assuming 1 m pond depths.

**Table 2.** Summary of the outputs generated through the application of the methodological framework for each construction phase. The number of individual catchments in each phase is denoted by 'n'.

| | | Construction Phase | | |
|---|---|---|---|---|
| | | **Phase 1** n = 10 | **Phase 2** n = 22 | **Phase 3** n = 22 |
| | | **Catchment Size** | | |
| Min | $m^2$ | 1731 | 1874 | 2724 |
| Max | $m^2$ | 40,236 | 35,932 | 16,578 |
| Mean | $m^2$ | 12,430 | 12,311 | 7101 |
| | | **Runoff Volume** | | |
| Min | $m^3$ | 45.6 | 49.4 | 71.8 |
| Max | $m^3$ | 1059.8 | 946.4 | 436.7 |
| Mean | $m^3$ | 327.4 | 324.3 | 187 |
| | | **Soil Loss per 3 Months** | | |
| Min | $m^3$ | 2.5 | 36.3 | 35.1 |
| Max | $m^3$ | 621.7 | 424.7 | 286.9 |
| Mean | $m^3$ | 140.7 | 195.1 | 35.1 |
| | | **Treatment Volume** | | |
| Min | $m^3$ | 68.9 | 86.1 | 106.8 |
| Max | $m^3$ | 1673.2 | 1226.4 | 723.6 |
| Mean | $m^3$ | 468.01 | 195.1 | 320.1 |
| | | **Treatment Volume to Accommodate Soil Loss** | | |
| Min | % | 3.7 | 21.1 | 32.9 |
| Max | % | 45 | 46.5 | 44.8 |
| Mean | % | 31.7 | 38.2 | 41.7 |
| | | **Catchment Area to Accommodate Treatment Volume (1 m Pond Depth)** | | |
| Min | % | 2.7 | 3.3 | 3.9 |
| Max | % | 4.8 | 4.9 | 4.8 |
| Mean | % | 4 | 4.3 | 4.5 |

Basic statistical analysis has been undertaken to determine the relationship between inputs of the methodological framework and to identify potential areas of weakness in the methodological process (Figure 4). This indicates that runoff volume is positively correlated with catchment area ($r^2 = 1$) (Figure 4a) which is to be expected considering a universal runoff coefficient has been applied across all catchments. This linear relationship does not exist when comparing soil loss and catchment area and runoff volume (Figure 4b,c). When catchment area exceeds 25,000 $m^2$, the corresponding soil loss volumes are lower than expected for three catchments. As the RULSE input parameters were universal, with the exception of the LS factor, this suggests that the discrepancy may be attributed to the catchment specific LS factor or another contributing factor. Examination of the LS factor indicates a positive correlation (Figure 4d) ($r^2 = 1$) with annual soil loss increasing with higher LS factors, which has been reported in other studies [24]. However, this does not account for the unexpected results shown in Figure 4b,c. A possible explanation for this could be the relatively lower LS factors for the catchments with areas exceeding 25,000 $m^2$, which could account for the below expected soil loss volumes in the larger catchments. For example, the LS factors for the catchments exceeding 25,000 $m^2$, which do not follow the linear relationship, are 7.74, 3.9 and 0.76 are below the mean LS value for all catchments, which is 9.5. When comparing the LS factor and catchment area (Figure 4e), it has been demonstrated that the LS factors within comparable catchment areas vary with the higher LS factors generally attributed to smaller catchments.

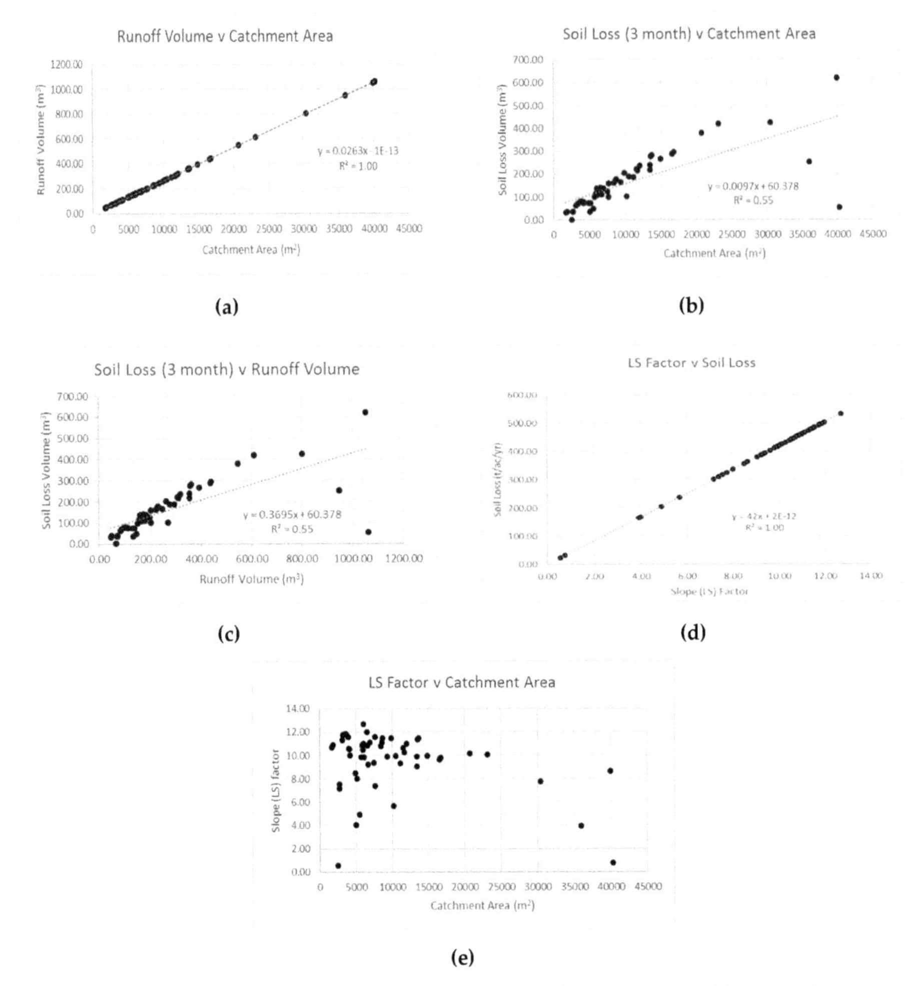


**Figure 4.** Relationships between elements of the methodological framework. (**a**) Runoff Volume v Catchment Area, (**b**) Soil Loss (3 Month) v Catchment Area, (**c**) Soil Loss (3 Month) v Runoff Volume, (**d**) LS factor v Soil Loss, (**e**) LS Factor v Catchment Area.

### 3.3. Sensitivity Analysis

As mentioned previously, the modelling approach used has included assumed input parameters. A sensitivity anaysis has been undertaken to assess what impacts different K factor and permeability input parameters (Table 3) have on the calculated runoff and soil loss volumes compared to the original input values (Table 1), which for the purposes of this excercise are considered the baseline. The input factors used for the sensitivity analysis represent the ranges provided in [1].

**Table 3.** Factor amendments applied for sensitivity analysis.

| Scenario | RUSLE K Factor | Permeability Factor | C Factor | Rationale |
|---|---|---|---|---|
| 1 (baseline) | 0.42 | 0.6 | | - |
| 2 | 0.2 | - | | Representative of gravelly sand |
| 3 | 0.6 | - | | Representative of silty-clay |
| 4<br>5 | -<br>- | 0.4<br>0.75 | | Range for stripped construction sites |
| 6 | - | - | 0.05 | Representative factor for woodchips, coir matting and mature crop cover |

The amended input parameters have been applied to all catchments (n = 57) to assess how runoff and soil loss volumes respond (Table 4). The summary results highlight the sensitivity of estimated soil loss in response to variations in the K factor with percentage changes in mean soil loss ranging between −53% and +43%. Simarly, permeability factor (scenarios 4 and 5) can result in marked differences in estimated runoff volumes. Given the differences in soil loss and runoff volumes presented, the results underline the importance of accurately representing site-specific conditions when adopting this approach for estimating the capacity of construction drainage. An additional sensitivity analysis has been included to test the potential impact the addition of the C factor could have (scenario 6). The C factor (0.05) has been used to provide an indication of the potential maximum soil loss reduction based on published C factor ranges [5], which show that a 95% reduction is soil loss could be achieved.

**Table 4.** Summary results of effect of input parameter amendments on soil loss volume and runoff volume. The results in () denote the percentage change compared to the baseline scenario.

| Scenario | Soil Loss Volume ($m^3$/3-Month) | | | Runoff Volume ($m^3$) | | |
|---|---|---|---|---|---|---|
| | Min | Max | Mean | Min | Max | Mean |
| 1 (baseline) | 2.5 | 621.7 | 159 | 45.6 | 1059.8 | 266.9 |
| 2 | 1.2<br>(−52) | 296.1<br>(−53) | 75.7<br>(−52) | 45.6<br>(0) | 1059.8<br>(0) | 266.9<br>(0) |
| 3 | 3.6<br>(+44) | 888.2<br>(+43) | 227.2<br>(+43) | 45.6<br>(0) | 1059.8<br>(0) | 266.9<br>(0) |
| 4 | 2.5<br>(0) | 621.7<br>(0) | 159<br>(0) | 30.4<br>(−33) | 706.5<br>(−33) | 178<br>(−33) |
| 5 | 2.5<br>(0) | 621.7<br>(0) | 159<br>(0) | 57<br>(+25) | 1324.8<br>(+25) | 333.7<br>(+25) |
| 6 | 0.13<br>(−95) | 31.1<br>(−95) | 8<br>(−95) | 45.6<br>(0) | 1059.8<br>(0) | 266.9<br>(0) |

Likewise, the results presented in Table 5 show that treatment volume, percentage of treatment volume required to accommodate soil loss and percentage of catchment areas required to accommodate treatment volume are responsive to input parameter changes. Scenarios 2 and 4 included reduced K factor and permeability coefficients, respectively.

**Table 5.** Sensitvity analysis of changes to treatment volume (Vt), treatment volume percentage required to accommodate soil loss and the percentage of catchment area required to accommodate treatment volume. Values in () represent percentage change in relation to baseline scenario.

| Scenario | Treatment Volume (Vt) ($m^3$) | | | Treatment Volume for Soil Loss (%) | | | % Catchment Area Required for Vt. | | |
|---|---|---|---|---|---|---|---|---|---|
| | Min | Max | Mean | Min | Max | Mean | Min | Max | Mean |
| 1 | 69 | 1673 | 426 | 3.7 | 46.5 | 38.5 | 2.7 | 4.9 | 4.3 |
| 2 | 61 (−11.6) | 1348 (−19.4) | 343 (−19.5) | 1.8 (−51.4) | 29.2 (−37.2) | 23.3 (−39.5) | 2.7 (0) | 3.7 (−24.5) | 3.4 (−20.9) |
| 3 | 70 (+1.4) | 1940 (+16) | 494 (+16) | 5.2 (+40.5) | 55.4 (+19.1) | 46.9 (+21.8) | 2.8 (+3.7) | 5.9 (+20.4) | 5.1 (+16.6) |
| 4 | 47 (−32.9) | 1323 (−21) | 337 (−20.9) | 5.4 (+45.9) | 56.6 (+21.7) | 48.1 (+24.9) | 1.9 (−29.6) | 4.0 (−18.4) | 3.5 (−18.6) |
| 5 | 85 (+23.2) | 1936 (+15.7) | 493 (+15.7) | 3 (−18.9) | 41 (−11.8) | 33.5 (−13) | 3.4 (−30) | 5.6 (+14.3) | 5.0 (+16.3) |
| 6 | 47 (−31.9) | 1083 (−35.3) | 275 (−35.4) | 0.2 (−94.6) | 4.2 (−91) | 3.1 (−91.9) | 2.6 (−3.7) | 2.7 (−44.9) | 2.7 (−37.2) |

For treatment volume (Table 5), the results show that the treatment volume was more responsive to a reduction in the permeability coefficient based on the percentage decreases compared to scenario 1. Increased input parameters (scenarios 3 and 5) show similar increases in treatment volume ($m^3$) with the exception of the minimum values, where more variability exists. The response of treatment volume to accommodate soil loss reflects the input parameter changes. The increase in treatment volume for soil loss (scenario 3) can be attributed to reduced runoff in reponse to a lower permeability factor. Considering the variability compared to scenario 1, the percentage of catchment area required to provide treatment in the form of settlement ponds, further emphasizes how important it is to represent site-specific conditions to avoid inaccuracies in capacity estimations. However, it should be noted that values presented exceed the required 1.5% of catchment area to accommodate settlement ponds as suggested [5]. This is based on the assumed depth of 1 m used in the case-study application. It is evident from the results presented in Table 5 that applying preventative stabilization measures (scenario 6) can result in relatively large reductions in treatment volume and the area within drainage catchments to accommodate treatment.

## 4. Discussion

The aim of this study was achieved through the development of a methodological framework to estimate the capacity of construction drainage to provide the volume to accommodate runoff and soil loss on an upcoming highway construction project.

The potential to apply RUSLE in the context of roads has previously been questioned [42]. Two reported areas of potential weakness in their application of the RUSLE on forest road plots include RUSLE developed for natural soils, and the scale of application in the study was smaller than RUSLE was originally intended for. When considering highway construction projects, topsoil is stripped and stored for re-application ahead of re-vegetation. Subsoils are then handled and relocated to form embanked fill areas. These fill areas can include fill materials from different source locations, all of which can have different characteristics and would be expected to have low organic matter content when compared with natural soils in an agricultural setting. Based on this, the robustness of RUSLE in a highway construction environment may be limited without refining how it is applied. However, through the scheme development process prior to construction, there can be several site visits for Ground Investigation surveys, which provides an opportunity to ground truth data to improve the robustness of the approach by providing more accurate input parameters.

Depending upon the design of the road, relatively discrete elevation changes due to cutting and embankment formations would lead to temporary drainage catchments with complex topographical features, which would need to be represented in the LS factor to estimate soil loss. The methodological framework includes the mean LS factor derived from an algorithm [31], using GIS software that uses pre-construction elevation data, which represents the land surface profile prior to construction activities commencing. Although this approach provides an indication of potential soil loss following site clearance, it does not reflect the topographical changes that would develop as construction progresses and slopes are formed. To resolve this issue, the model would need to consider each pre-constructed slope feature separately, which would be further removed from the original field application that RUSLE was intended for [42]. Alternatively, it may be possible to create a DTM using proposed design elevations that are developed during the highway design process rather than existing ground levels. This could potentially improve the accuracy of the model as previous studies [22] found that slope gradient was a significant factor affecting sediment yield from a cut slope.

A source of uncertainty also exists in deriving the input parameters used in the methodological framework. A broad range of K factors from 0.2 (gravelly sand) to 0.6 for silty clay are provided in [1]. The selected K factor (0.42), is based on a silty loam soil with 2% organic matter content [40]. K factors for silty loam soils range from 0.43–0.64, with 0.64 being attributed to a range of soils with a silty loam texture of lacustrine or stream terrace deposit origins. This could be a better representation of soils on site based on the superficial deposits underlying the site, which consist of alluvium and glaciofluvial deposits. When applying the K factor in a construction setting, it is important to consider those activities on site which could affect the selection of the most appropriate K factor(s). For example, the K factors [1] provide representative K factors for topsoil, which, when applied to a highway construction setting, will not necessarily correspond to the exposed surface after topsoil stripping. It was reported that exposed subsoils can be considerably different from the topsoil, which could lead to under-representation of erodibility if topsoil-derived K factor(s) are applied [20]. The K factor includes multiple parameters, including Particle Size Distribution (PSD). Ground investigation data collected during various stages leading up to highway construction, could prove beneficial for future applications of the methodological framework by providing representative PSD data from underlying soil profile layers. This could improve the robustness of the methodology by adding site-specific parameters. Furthermore, the authors suggest that this approach can be applied to cuttings to assess how soil erosion can vary depending upon cut depth. K factors relating to cuttings could also in theory be used to estimate erosion from embankments that are formed from material excavated from cut areas. However, due to re-working and subsequent compaction to meet engineered slope design specifications, it is doubtful that the fill material will retain its original in situ characteristics.

An additional potential benefit of utilizing ground investigation data is its application to refine the sizing of the temporary settlement ponds. Currently, the approach does not consider the retention time that would be required to facilitate settlement of suspended materials. Since the retention time required to achieve settlement is dependent on particle size and settlement velocity [1], PSD data obtained during ground investigations could be used to provide a site-specific approach for settlement pond design. Applying this approach could further improve the robustness of the methodological framework, as currently settlement rate is not considered.

An additional assumption includes the universal application of the annual average R factor (Table 1). Published annual R factor values [26] for the site location exceed 200, which is considerably higher than the selected input factor, which could result in soil loss underestimation. In addition, the universal application does not account for the seasonal variations reported which include R values below 40 for spring and up to 160 for autumn months [26]. Based on this, due to the dynamic nature of construction activities, applying an annual R factor does not necessarily reflect the time period where construction activities would be underway and applying seasonal values may prove more accurate. To reduce any bias from manipulating the annual estimated soil loss. It has been highlighted that the reliance on sediment controls including settlement ponds or treatment solutions can be reduced through the implementation of preventative erosion control [5]. These can include woodchips, coir matting and seeding, which have all be shown to have potentially significant benefits in reducing soil loss which is evident from the sensitivity analysis (Table 4; Table 5). Given the proportion of treatment volume required to accommodate soil loss and the percentage of catchment areas required to provide treatment (Table 5), there is scope to reduce losses, through the application of erosion control measures. As previously mentioned, C and P factors were not included at this stage, however, incorporating these factors provides a valuable opportunity to add further accuracy in the RUSLE application through the representation on on-site practices. As shown in [4], the management practice used can either reduce, or increase soil loss. A P factor of 1.2 (20% soil loss increase) should be applied to compact slope areas that have been smoothed across the slope by machinery would be a better representation of on-site conditions in these areas, which could include filled embankments. Similar to the RUSLE application [4,21], incorporating C factors would allow designers to identify what cover practices should be adopted to reduce soil loss. For example, the application of woodchips (C = 0.08) [4] can reduce soil loss by approximately 90%. Biodegradable textiles (coir matting), can result in 80–90% reduction in soil loss on slopes > 15% [7], which reflect representative highway construction engineered slopes with gradients 1:2.5 and 1:3 (40% and 33%, respectively). The effectiveness of re-vegetation, either temporary seeding or permanent, is dependent upon the stage of development. For example, soil loss after seedbed preparation may be negligible; however, as the vegetation crop matures and the crop canopy increases, soil loss may be reduced by approximately 95% [4]. Therefore, adopting this approach would prove to be most beneficial if seeding (temporary or permanent) was undertaken soon after final construction had ceased in an area, or if exposed areas would be left dormant for a period of time before construction continues [7]. Little or no soil loss reduction can be expected after initial seed bed preparation, with soil loss reductions nearing 95% as the cover crop matures [4].

An important consideration when estimating the size of construction drainage features is the calculation of runoff volume. Temporary drainage features will need to accommodate the volume of water and it is therefore necessary to design to a specific rainfall event. The application of a single rainfall depth (Table 1) to the study site was deemed appropriate as any variations in depths are likely to be relatively minimal, given the relatively small geographic extent of the highway construction project. As catchment area and runoff volume were positively correlated (Figure 4a), variations in rainfall depth would have a direct impact on the treatment volume required within each drainage catchment, which would impact the land area required to provide the treatment presented in Table 2, which may be over- or underestimated.

The Rational Method [35,36] has known weaknesses in determining the runoff or permeability coefficient, which changes depending upon storm duration and the conservative estimation of runoff. It could be argued that for the purposes of this study, a conservative estimation provides a level of security by preventing the underestimation of runoff volume, which is used to size construction drainage. However, it is recommended that alternative methods are considered when applied to rural areas [38].

## 5. Conclusions

The methodological framework provides temporary drainage designers with a useful tool to estimate the size of construction drainage to ensure that sufficient land is available to accommodate construction drainage features. However, this study has highlighted where improvements could be made to increase the robustness of the modelling approach used. The framework incorporates the RULSE, which was originally developed for application on natural soils in an agricultural setting and uses assumed input parameters to represent site-specific conditions. The use of assumed input parameters adds an element of uncertainty to the model outputs, which could be improved by incorporating site-specific data that would provide a more accurate representation of the subsoils exposed during construction. Furthermore, the LS factor that has been applied to each temporary drainage catchment is based on existing topography and therefore does not account for any ground profile changes during construction. During highway construction, the creation of engineered slopes (cuttings and embankments) are created, which, if left exposed, are prone to water erosion. If slope features were included in the model, this could identify areas where additional controls could be deployed to protect the receiving environment. A universal rainfall depth has been applied to the study area to estimate runoff volume. Given the relatively constrained geographic reach of the construction project, it would be unlikely that any discrete rainfall depth variations would be encountered. However, to reduce any uncertainty that this approach brings, rainfall depths could be obtained from various other locations along the study area extent. The sensitivity analysis has shown the potential benefits that can be achieved through the implementation of effective erosion control. As the industry relies heavily on the use of temporary settlement ponds, which can have limited effectiveness, effective erosion control could reduce soil loss and help protect the water environment.

**Author Contributions:** Conceptualization, S.M. and M.W.; methodology, M.W., D.L. and S.F.; validation, M.W., D.L. and S.F.; formal analysis, M.W.; investigation, M.W.; resources, M.W. and S.M.; data curation, M.W., D.L. and S.F.; writing—original draft preparation, M.W., S.M., A.M. and I.M.; writing—review and editing, M.W., S.M., A.M. and and I.M.; visualization, M.W. and S.F.; supervision, S.M., A.M. and I.M.; project administration, M.W. and S.M.; funding acquisition, S.M., A.M. All authors have read and agreed to the published version of the manuscript.

**Funding:** This research was funded by Innovate UK, grant number KTP010752.

**Acknowledgments:** The authors wish to thank the generous support of Jacobs UK Ltd., without whom, this research would not have been possible.

**Conflicts of Interest:** The authors declare no conflict of interest.

## References and Notes

1. Murnane, E.; Heap, A.; Swain, A. *Control of Water Pollution from Linear Construction Projects: Technical Guidance*; CIRIA: London, UK, 2006.
2. European Commission Best Environmental Management Practice for the Building and Construction Sector. 2012. *29136*. Available online: https://data.europa.eu/doi/10.2760/50247 (accessed on 12 October 2019).
3. Woods-Ballard, B. *The Suds Manual*; CIRIA: London, England, 2015.
4. Lake, D.W. *New York State Standards and Specifications for Erosion and Sediment Control*; Empire State Chapter Soil and Water Conservation Society: Albany, NY, USA, 2016.
5. Pitt, R.; Clark, S.E.; Lake, D. *Construction Site Erosion and Sediment Controls: Planning, Design and Performance*; DEStech Publications: Lancaster, PA, USA, 2007; pp. 52–54.
6. Kalainesan, S.; Neufeld, R.D.; Quimpo, R.; Yodnane, P. Sedimentation basin performance at highway construction sites. *J. Environ. Manag.* **2009**, *90*, 838–849. [CrossRef] [PubMed]
7. United States Environmental Protection Agency. *Developing your Stormwater Pollution Prevention Plan: A Guide for Construction Sites*; United States Environmental Protection Agency: Albany, NY, USA, 2007.
8. Anonymous. The Limits of Settling. *Watershed Prot. Tech.* **1997**, *2*, 30. Available online: https://search.proquest.com/docview/196797102 (accessed on 26 June 2020).
9. Highways Agency; The Scottish Office Development Department; The Welsh Office; The Department of the Environment for Northern Ireland. Design Manual for Roads and Bridges. Available online: https://www.standardsforhighways.co.uk/dmrb/ (accessed on 10 November 2019).
10. (Jacobs UK Ltd.). Personal communication, 2019. (Note)
11. Noble, B.; Hill, M.; Nielsen, J. Environmental assessment framework for identifying and mitigating the effects of linear development to wetlands. *Landsc. Urban Plan.* **2011**, *99*, 133–140. [CrossRef]
12. Volk, M.; Möller, M.; Wurbs, D. A pragmatic approach for soil erosion risk assessment within policy hierarchies. *Land Use Policy* **2010**, *27*, 997–1009. [CrossRef]
13. Mickovski, S.B.; Thomson, C.S. Developing a framework for the sustainability assessment of eco-engineering measures. *Ecol. Eng.* **2017**, *109*, 145–160. Available online: https://browzine.com/articles/159482471 (accessed on 5 February 2020). [CrossRef]
14. Vogt, J.V.; Colombo, R.; Bertolo, F. Deriving drainage networks and catchment boundaries: A new methodology combining digital elevation data and environmental characteristics. *Geomorphology* **2003**, *53*, 281–298. [CrossRef]
15. Kouli, M.; Soupios, P.; Vallianatos, F. Soil erosion prediction using the Revised Universal Soil Loss Equation (RUSLE) in a GIS framework, Chania, Northwestern Crete, Greece. *Environ. Geol.* **2009**, *57*, 483–497. Available online: https://search.proquest.com/docview/210843828 (accessed on 18 January 2020). [CrossRef]

16. SEPA. Personal communication, 2019. (Note)
17. Renard, K.G.; Foster, G.R.; Weesies, G.A.; McCool, D.K.; Yoder, D.C. *Predicting Soil Erosion by Water: A Guide to Conservation Planning with the Revised Universal Soil Loss Equation (RUSLE)*; Agricultural Handbook No. 703, Agricultural Research Service USDA: Washington, DC, USA, 1997.
18. Scottish Government. Scottish Planning Policy. Available online: https://www.gov.scot/publications/scottish-planning-policy/ (accessed on 17 November 2019).
19. SEPA. Personal communication II, 2020. (Note)
20. Wischmeier, W.H.; Smith, D.D. *Predicting Rainfall Erosion Losses: A Guide to Conservation Planning*; Department of Agriculture, Science and Education Administration: Washington, DC, USA, 1978.
21. Greenville County. Stormwater Management Design Manual. Available online: https://www.greenvillecounty.org/LandDevelopment/DesignManual.aspx (accessed on 19 October 2018).
22. Megahan, W.F.; Wilson, M.; Monsen, S.B. Sediment production from granitic cutslopes on forest roads in Idaho, USA. *Earth Surf. Process. Landf.* **2001**, *26*, 153–163. [CrossRef]
23. Yoon, K.S.; Kim, C.W.; Woo, H. Application of RUSLE for Erosion Estimation of Construction Sites in Coastal Catchments. *J. Coast. Res.* **2009**, *SI*, 1696–1700. Available online: https://www.jstor.org/stable/25738079 (accessed on 17 November 2019).
24. Chehlafi, A.; Kchikach, A.; Derradji, A.; Mequedade, N. Highway cutting slopes with high rainfall erosion in Morocco: Evaluation of soil losses and erosion control using concrete arches. *Eng. Geol.* **2019**, *260*, 105200. [CrossRef]
25. Panagos, P.; Borrelli, P.; Poesen, J.; Ballabio, C.; Lugato, E.; Meusburger, K.; Montanarella, L.; Alewell, C. The new assessment of soil loss by water erosion in Europe. *Environ. Sci. Policy* **2015**, *54*, 438–447. [CrossRef]
26. Panagos, P.; Ballabio, C.; Borrelli, P.; Meusburger, K.; Klik, A.; Rousseva, S.; Tadić, M.P.; Michaelides, S.; Hrabalíková, M.; Olsen, P.; et al. Rainfall erosivity in Europe. *Sci. Total Environ.* **2015**, *511*, 801–814. [CrossRef] [PubMed]
27. Benavidez, R.; Jackson, B.; Maxwell, D.; Norton, K. A review of the (Revised) Universal Soil Loss Equation ((R)USLE): With a view to increasing its global applicability and improving soil loss estimates. *Hydrol. Earth Syst. Sci.* **2018**, *22*, 6059–6086. Available online: https://search.proquest.com/docview/2137760130 (accessed on 10 June 2020). [CrossRef]
28. Scottish Environment Protection Agency. Supporting Guidance (WAT-SG-75) Sector Specific Guidance: Construction Sites. Available online: https://www.sepa.org.uk/regulations/water/pollution-control/construction-site-licences/ (accessed on 20 November 2018).
29. Jacobs UK Ltd. *A9 Dualling Programme Tay Crossing to Ballinluig Constructability Report Appendix G Land Requirements for Construction SuDS*; Jacobs UK Ltd: Glasgow, Scotland, 2018. (Note).
30. Pittner, C.; Allerton, G. *SUDS for roads*; WSP UK Ltd.: Edinburgh, Scotland, 2009.
31. Desmet, P.J.; Govers, G. A GIS procedure for automatically calculating the USLE LS factor on topographically complex landscape units. *J. Soil Water Conserv.* **1996**, *51*, 427–433.
32. Transport Scotland. A9 Dualling Programme: Tay Crossing to Ballinluig DMRB Stage 3 Environmental Statement. Available online: https://www.transport.gov.scot/publication/draft-orders-and-environmental-statement-a9-tay-crossing-to-ballinluig/ (accessed on 7 September 2019).
33. Dąbrowska, J.; Dąbek, P.B.; Lejcuś, I. A GIS based approach for the mitigation of surface runoff to a shallow lowland reservoir. *Ecohydrol. Hydrobiol.* **2018**, *18*, 420–430. [CrossRef]
34. Graf, L.; Moreno-de-las-Heras, M.; Ruiz, M.; Calsamiglia, A.; García-Comendador, J.; Fortesa, J.; López-Tarazón, J.; Estrany, J. Accuracy Assessment of Digital Terrain Model Dataset Sources for Hydrogeomorphological Modelling in Small Mediterranean Catchments. *Remote Sens.* **2018**, *10*, 2014. Available online: https://search.proquest.com/docview/2303929457 (accessed on 19 February 2020). [CrossRef]
35. Mulvany, T. On the use of self registering rain and flood gauges in making observations of the relation of rainfall and flood discharges in given catchment. *Trans. Inst. Civ. Eng. Irel.* **1851**, *4*, 18–33.
36. Kuichling, E. The relation between the rainfall and the discharge of sewers in populous districts. *Trans. Am. Soc. Civ. Eng.* **1889**, *20*, 1–56.
37. Brutsaert, W. *Hydrology: An introduction*; Cambridge University Press: Cambridge, UK, 2005; pp. 346–477.
38. Kellagher, R. *Storage Requirements for Rainfall Runoff from Greenfield Development Sites*; Report SR 580; HR Wallingford: Wallingford, England, 2002.

39. Scottish Natural Heritage. Sitelink. Available online: https://sitelink.nature.scot/site/8366 (accessed on 16 January 2020).
40. Stewart, B.A.; Woolhiser, D.A.; Wischmeier, W.H.; Caro, J.H.; Freere, M.H. *Control of Water Pollution from Cropland*; Report EPA-600; Department of Agriculture, Agricultural Research Service: Washington, DC, USA, 1975; Volume I.
41. UK Centre for Ecology and Hydrology. Flood Estimation Handbook Web Service. Available online: https://fehweb.ceh.ac.uk/ (accessed on 6 October 2018).
42. Riedel, M.S. *Collaborative Research and Watershed Management for Optimization of Forest Road Best Management Practices*; International Conference on Ecology and Transportation, Centre for Transportation and the Environment; North Carolina State University: Raleigh, NC, USA, 2003; pp. 148–158.

MDPI
St. Alban-Anlage 66
4052 Basel
Switzerland
Tel. +41 61 683 77 34
Fax +41 61 302 89 18
www.mdpi.com

*Sustainability* Editorial Office
E-mail: sustainability@mdpi.com
www.mdpi.com/journal/sustainability

Lightning Source UK Ltd.
Milton Keynes UK
UKHW052306141022
410485UK00003B/82